To my sweet grandchildren
my adorable Liah & Kalyb
I'll miss you so much when you
move to the island of geckos,
palm trees and sunshine.
All my love forever & ever,
Grandma ♡

ISLAND HERITAGE™
PUBLISHING
A DIVISION OF THE MADDEN CORPORATION

94-411 Kōʻaki Street
Waipahu, Hawaiʻi 96797-2806
Orders: (800) 468-2800
Information: (808) 564-8800
Fax: (808) 564-8877
islandheritage.com

ISBN: 1-61710-237-7
First Edition, Fourth Printing—2017
COP 171003

The Gecko Who Wanted To Be Different

written by Dorothy Sarna Saurer
illustrated by Don Robinson

ISLAND HERITAGE™
PUBLISHING

Kupu the Gecko was feeling so sad.

Great geckos galore! What a problem he had!

He had a great body, so long and so thin,

But what he disliked was the look of his skin.

First Kupu would moan, and then he would groan,
And then he would say in a very sad tone,
"What color are geckos? We're not on the chart.
We're all gecko-colored – can't tell us apart!
Gecko-color is really no color at all –
We always just seem to blend in with the wall.

4

Why couldn't I have been a goldfish so bright
Or a zebra, who's striped like the day and the night?
Cats come in colors, and so do the dogs,
And oh! The beautiful *green* skin of frogs!
Or the sunshiny yellow of a new baby duck.
And chameleons *change* colors! Talk about luck.
Looking like everyone else makes me mad.
Why couldn't I have been checkered or plaid?

Leopards stand out because they have spots –
I wish they would share them because they have LOTS.
Every gecko I see looks just like my twin –
Oh, how I wish I had different skin!

The colors of butterflies are such a sight
And peacocks and eagles are so fine and bright.
Penguins, in tuxes, look always dressed up.

And all those cute spots on a Dalmatian pup!
Bumble bees glisten in yellow and black –
While geckos are dull from their front to their back.

Lions are kings with their long golden manes,
While geckos just look like a bunch of plain Janes!
Why am I such a plain-colored lizard?

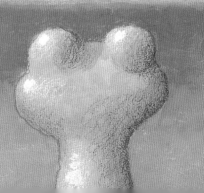

Oh, how I wish I could meet with a wizard!
He could snap his long fingers and then – BEHOLD!
My skin would turn colors – perhaps even GOLD!"

"That's it!" Kupu thought as he danced and he twirled.
"I'll be known as Gold Gecko all over the world!
I want to look different, all shiny and bold,
And, wow! I'd sure look that way if I'm gold!"

14

Soon there was nothing else Kupu could think of.
He wanted some gold skin that fit like a glove.
He lost all his friends, who thought he was boring,
"It's worse," said one pal, "than my big sister's snoring!"
They all thought his dream was nothing but sin,
Shouldn't geckos be happy in plain gecko skin?

One day when his mood was especially grim,
His father decided to go talk to him.
"Kupu," he said, "Why make such a fuss?
You're acting as if you're ashamed of us."

"Oh, no!" said Kupu, who loved Mom and Dad,
"You're the very best parents a guy ever had!

But every gecko looks just like my twin.
I want to be *different* with colorful skin.
We all look the same!" he said with a groan,
"I want to look like *just me alone*."

And poor Kupu looked so sad and so blue,
His father said, "I know just what to do.
We can't change the color or shade of your skin,
But we *can* stop you from looking like everyone's twin."
"How?" Kupu asked, knowing Dad was so smart.
"I want to be different with all of my heart."

"OK," his Dad said, "Tomorrow you'll see…
I'll bring something special for you home with me."
Then he added, with a very big smile,
"Gecko color is always in style.
And we're each of us special, though we look just the same.
Not one other gecko here has your name!"

Kupu thought hard about what Dad had said,
And many new thoughts got mixed up in his head.
"Maybe my skin color isn't so bad…
After all, I look exactly like Dad,
And he's always special, I know without fail,
From the top of his head to the end of his tail."

"I miss all my friends and do want to play!
Maybe I'll be different in some other way…
Maybe I'll be a big movie star!
That's a good dream, and I could go far!"

And so with a smile, Kupu fell asleep
And soon he was counting look-alike sheep.

The next day he paced as he waited for Dad,
And when he came home, Kupu was so glad!

"Dad!" he exclaimed, with widening eyes,
"What's in the box? Oh! What's the surprise?"
He tore open the box and ripped off the bow,
And seeing inside, gasped a big "OHHH!"

The box held a colorful T-shirt, brand new.
Dad said, "This was made special for you.
It has your name in bright red on the chest."
"Wow, Dad!" Kupu said, "This works the best!"

He put on the T-shirt and grinned a big grin.
He was no longer worried about his drab skin.
Kupu was happy as happy could be –
"NOW EVERYONE KNOWS I'M REALLY ME!"

The End

THE IMPACT OF ENVIRONMENTALISM:

TRANSPORTATION

Andrew Solway

Chicago, Illinois

www.capstonepub.com
Visit our website to find out more information about Heinemann-Raintree books.

To order:
☎ Phone 800-747-4992
🖳 Visit www.capstonepub.com to browse our catalog and order online.

Edited by Andrew Farrow, Adam Miller, and
 Diyan Leake
Designed by Victoria Allen
Picture research by Elizabeth Alexander
Illustrations by Oxford Designers & Illustrators

Originated by Capstone Global Library Ltd
Printed and bound in China by Leo Paper Products Ltd

16 15 14 13 12
10 9 8 7 6 5 4 3 2 1

Library of Congress Cataloging-in-Publication Data

Solway, Andrew.
 Transportation / Andrew Solway.
  p. cm.—(The impact of environmentalism)
 Includes bibliographical references and index.
 ISBN 978-1-4329-6520-4 (hb)—ISBN 978-1-4329-6526-6 (pb) 1. Transportation—Environmental aspects--Juvenile literature. 2. Pollution—Juvenile literature. 3. Environmentalism—Juvenile literature. I. Title.
 HE147.65.S65 2013
 363.73'1—dc23   2012001043

Acknowledgments
The author and publisher are grateful to the following for permission to reproduce copyright material: Alamy pp. 7 (© David R. Frazier Photolibrary, Inc.), 13 (© Caro), 20 (© Mark Boulton), 39 (© D. Burke), 51 (© AlamyCelebrity); Foster + Partners p. 52; Getty Images pp. 11 (Hulton Archive), 25 (Bloomberg News/ Mark Elias), 37 (Bloomberg/Michele Tantussi), 41 top (Science & Society Picture Library), 41 bottom (Bloomberg News/Adeel Halim), 50 (AFP/ Frank Perry); © Greenpeace p. 14; Nature Picture Library p. 23 (© Ingo Arndt); Press Association Images p. 16 (Tim Ockenden/PA Archive); Photolibrary pp. 32 (Reso Reso), 44 (Lineair/Ron Giling), 57 (Ticket/Warwick Kent); Science Photo Library p. 35 (Matteis/Look at Sciences); Shutterstock p. 21 (© Dongliu); Siemens Press Picture p. 49; © Copyright United Technologies Corporation. Used with permission p. 27; University of Warwick p. 29; World Solar Challenge Australia p. 54.

Cover photograph of (top) exhaust fumes, reproduced with permission of iStockphoto (© David Parsons), and (bottom) electric trains in Zagreb, Croatia, reproduced with permission of Shutterstock (© bubamarac).

Every effort has been made to contact copyright holders of material reproduced in this book. Any omissions will be rectified in subsequent printings if notice is given to the publisher.

CONTENTS

Words printed in **bold** are explained in the glossary.

TRANSPORTATION TODAY

Open up your refrigerator or pantry and you might find beans from South America, apples from New Zealand, or cheese from Switzerland. Your shoes may have come from Vietnam, the family car could be from Japan, and your cell phone may be from Finland. Without fast, cheap transportation, we would not have any of these things.

We also need transportation to move ourselves around. Many people live in the country but work in the city, take vacations in far-away places, and take regular trips to visit family or friends.

Concentrated energy

Nearly all our modern methods of transportation rely on engines powered by fuels. The most important fuels are coal, oil, and gas, the three **fossil fuels**. Without fossil fuels, modern transportation would not be possible.

Fossil fuels are very good sources of energy. They are easy to extract, they are fairly cheap, and they are available in huge quantities. However, fossil fuels also have serious problems.

Big drawbacks

First, fossil fuels are not **renewable**. Once they run out, they cannot be replaced. In the past 150 years, we have used up huge amounts of fossil fuels. We could run out of oil, the most important fossil fuel, in the near future.

Second, fossil fuels produce polluting gases when they burn. The biggest pollutant is carbon dioxide. Carbon dioxide in the atmosphere acts as a **greenhouse gas**, trapping some of the Sun's heat. The extra carbon dioxide released from burning fossil fuels is making Earth warmer. If carbon dioxide **emissions** continue, the world will get too hot for humans.

Peak oil

The gasoline and diesel that fuel most of our transportation are made from crude oil. However, oil is the fossil fuel that is most in danger of running out. Some experts think that we have already reached maximum production levels for crude oil. Many of the world's major oil fields are producing less oil than they have in the past—and new oil fields are not being discovered as quickly as old ones run out. It is getting more and more difficult to keep oil production at current levels. At some point, the amount of oil we can produce will begin to fall.

The impact of environmentalism

Environmentalists are people who are working to slow down or stop our destruction of the natural world. In the 1950s, the environmental movement was very small, but it has since grown rapidly. Today, millions of people are environmentalists, from students and scientists to politicians and retired people.

Modern forms of transportation have a great impact on the environment. Engines burning fossil fuels emit carbon dioxide that causes **global warming**. Other gas emissions cause pollution that kills wildlife, damages human health, and causes **acid rain**. The roads, railroad tracks, docks, airports, oil refineries, gasoline stations, and other structures that support the transportation network also cause damage to the environment.

So, what have environmentalists done to try to reduce the damage that transportation does to the environment? And how successful have they been?

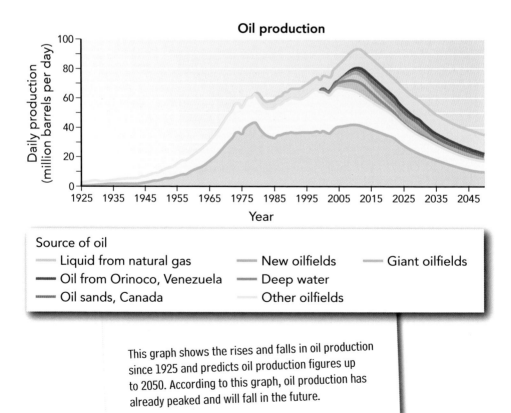

This graph shows the rises and falls in oil production since 1925 and predicts oil production figures up to 2050. According to this graph, oil production has already peaked and will fall in the future.

THE SCALE OF THE PROBLEM

If you have ever walked along a busy road or down a street where there is a traffic jam, you will have noticed some of the major problems that transportation brings. The air is smelly and unpleasant, because it is full of the exhaust gases from the vehicles. The noise of the traffic is loud and sometimes deafening. You can feel big trucks making the ground vibrate as they rumble past. And the sheer numbers of vehicles on the road cause **congestion**.

Exhaust emissions

The emissions you see coming out of a vehicle's exhaust pipes are mainly solid particles of carbon—soot and smoke. These "**particulates**" are small enough to float and mix with the air, causing **smog**, which can lead to human health problems.

The waste gases that you cannot see also are a big problem. Cars, vans, buses, and trucks produce a blend of polluting gases. Whenever a vehicle starts up, it begins pouring these exhaust gases into the atmosphere.

Burning is a chemical reaction of a fuel with oxygen from the air, so many of the gases formed are **oxides**. The most important of these gases is carbon dioxide. Transportation produces about one-quarter of all carbon dioxide emissions. Other gases include carbon monoxide, a gas that can cause breathing difficulties.

Reducing particulates

Smoke and soot were much bigger problems in the past than they are today. Until the 1950s, the biggest source of particulates in many Western countries was the smoke from coal fires. Smoke and soot from fires blackened buildings and caused smog and choking pollution.

In 1952, London, England, was hit by the "Great London Smog." During this time, deaths rose to three or four times normal levels. In 1953, a similar smog episode happened in New York City, killing between 170 and 260 people. Then, in 1954, smog caused Los Angeles, California, to virtually shut down for a month. As a result, the United Kingdom and United States passed laws to reduce the amount of particulates released into the air (see page 14).

There are also oxides of nitrogen and sulfur that are the main causes of acid rain. Nitrogen and sulfur oxides are greenhouse gases, like carbon dioxide. They are part of the world's biggest pollution problem—the warming of Earth's climate.

The world's worst cities for particulate pollution (smoke and soot)	
City	Particulate matter (micrograms per cubic meter)
Ulan Bator, Mongolia	279
Cairo, Egypt	169
Delhi, India	150
Kolkata, India	128
Tianjin, China	125
Chongqing, China	123
Kanpur, India	109
Lucknow, India	109
Jakarta, Indonesia	104
Shenyang, China	101

The haze over the city of Los Angeles is caused by pollution from car exhausts.

Global warming

The effect of carbon dioxide and other greenhouse gases on Earth's climate is called global warming or **climate change**.

The changing climate is already beginning to have some effects on the world's weather. The eight warmest years ever recorded have all occurred since 1998. The years 2005 and 2010 were the hottest years ever recorded, while 1998, 2002, 2003, 2006, 2007, and 2009 all tied for third place. There have also been particular hot spots. In 2003, a heat wave in Europe killed over 35,000 people. In the same year, 1,300 people died in a heat wave in India. In June 2006, there was another heat wave across Europe, followed by a heat wave across North America. In 2010, Russia had its worst heat wave in 1,000 years.

Not just warming

Scientists take millions of measurements at thousands of weather stations every year. These measurements show that, overall, the average temperature of the whole world is gradually rising.

Global warming does not simply mean that everywhere gets warmer. There have been some sizzling summers in recent years, but also some ice-cold winters. There have been droughts, but also heavy rainfall and flooding. This is because the climate may slowly be warming, but the *weather* can vary greatly from year to year.

However, extreme weather events do seem to be happening more frequently as the climate changes. Large storms, heavy rainfall, and long periods of drought are becoming more and more common.

Global effects

Climate change is already making itself felt. Some of the biggest effects have been in the Arctic and Antarctic, where ice fields, ice caps, and glaciers have already begun to melt. Sea level has risen about .07 inch (1.8 millimeters) per year for the last 100 years, and it will continue rising for at least 100 years to come.

In the future, the effects of global warming could get worse. Millions of people could suffer from famine because of drought, while millions more may be made homeless by flooding. The changed climate will affect the **habitats** of many animals and birds, and some species will not survive the changes.

If we want to prevent the worst effects of climate change, we need to reduce the amounts of greenhouse gases we release into the atmosphere. This is one of the biggest challenges the human race has ever faced.

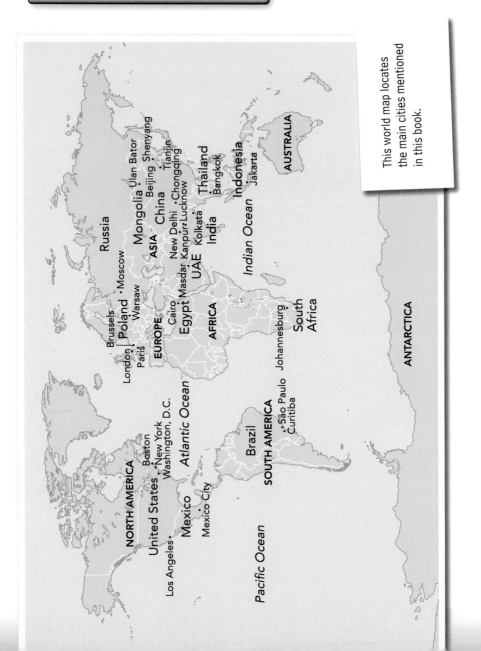

This world map locates the main cities mentioned in this book.

Other problems of transportation

Polluting emissions are not the only problems caused by transportation. Traffic in cities also causes congestion. Major cities around the world suffer from traffic jams. In cities such as São Paulo in Brazil or Beijing in China, jams can be up to 160 miles (100 kilometers) long. One traffic jam in Beijing lasted for nine days. Huge amounts of time and money are wasted as people sit in traffic on their way to and from work.

No.	City	Country
The world's 15 worst cities for traffic jams		
1.	São Paulo	Brazil
2.	Beijing	China
3.	Brussels	Belgium
4.	Paris	France
5.	Warsaw	Poland
6.	Mexico City	Mexico
7.	Los Angeles	United States
8.	Moscow	Russia
9.	London	United Kingdom
10.	New Delhi	India
11.	New York City	United States
12.	Johannesburg	South Africa
13.	Bangkok	Thailand
14.	Washington, D.C.	United States
15.	Wrocław	Poland

Noise is another kind of pollution produced by transportation. Noise is unwanted sound. It may not seem like a very serious problem, but noise pollution makes people feel stressed. Over time, it can damage their hearing. Road traffic is one of the most widespread sources of noise. Researchers have found that over 40 percent of people are bothered by traffic noise. Fewer people are affected by aircraft noise, but it can be much louder and can even cause hearing damage.

Huge amounts of land and natural habitat have been destroyed to make room for roads, railroad lines, parking lots, and other parts of the transportation network. In addition to taking up space, roads and railroads divide up the landscape. Many animals are killed crossing roads as they try to move from one area to another.

More people, more transportation

In 1999, the world population reached 6 billion people, and it continues to grow. By 2099, the population is likely be around 9 billion. The transportation systems in most cities and towns are already struggling to cope. Roads and railroads are carrying far more traffic than they were designed for. As populations grow, this problem will get even worse.

Economic growth also leads to transportation problems. As countries get richer, more people can afford to buy cars and to travel on trains and airplanes. So, in countries with high economic growth, pollution and other problems related to transportation are growing fast—even without population growth.

Then and Now
Old jams

Problems of traffic congestion and pollution are not new. There were horse-drawn jams in London and other European cities as early as the 1650s. Some were nearly as bad as today's traffic jams:

"Went this evening to see the illuminations, but the streets were so crowded with people and carriages that it was impossible to move. The throng was so great that I got to a lamp post and there I had to hang for half an hour before the road was clear that I could get [back onto the carriage]… I went out at nine o'clock and got back at eleven. In that time I did not get more than half a mile."

William Tayler, May 24, 1837, London

A drawing from 1835 shows London Bridge clogged with horse-drawn traffic.

PROVIDING THE POWER

For environmentalists, engines are the biggest problem with transportation. But why is this? To find out, we need to look more closely at what engines do and how they work.

Engines can do amazing things. They can move over 10,000 tons of cargo from the United States to Australia, or fly 500 passengers across the Atlantic Ocean. Cars, trucks, boats, and aircraft are all powered by engines that burn fuel to produce **kinetic energy** (movement). There are two basic kinds of engine used in transportation—**internal combustion (IC) engines** and gas turbines.

Controlled explosions

Gasoline and diesel engines are IC engines. The "combustion" (burning) is an explosion of a mixture of fuel and air. This happens inside the engine in a small chamber called a cylinder.

When the fuel and air mixture explodes, it expands very quickly. The expanding gases push on a piston at the bottom of the cylinder and move it downward. The piston turns a crankshaft, which goes around and around. Fuel and air go into the engine, and rotary motion comes out.

Gas turbines

Jet engines are gas turbine engines. A turbine is a fan with many narrow blades. When a stream of gas flows through the turbine, it spins like a high-speed windmill.

In a jet engine, fuel and air are burned together in a combustion chamber. The hot gases from the combustion rush out through the back of the engine. The jet of hot gas shooting out backwards pushes the aircraft forward.

Not all useful

Although engines are very useful, they have two problems that cause damage to the environment. The first is that most engines burn fossil fuels. We have seen that this is bad for the environment, because the burning fuel is turned into carbon dioxide and other polluting gases.

The other big problem with engines is that they are not very energy-**efficient**. A large amount of the energy used to fuel the engine is wasted as heat rather than being turned into movement. Three-quarters of the energy used to power an engine is wasted.

Then and Now
Early biofuels

Rudolf Diesel, who invented the diesel engine, fueled his early engines with peanut oil. However, diesel oil made from petroleum was cheaper, so it soon became the most common fuel. Today, some cars can run on biodiesel (see page 32), which produces fewer carbon emissions than normal diesel. Biodiesel is made from plant oils—so diesel fuel has come full circle.

Jet engines can go through 800 gallons (3,000 liters) of fuel per hour. All the waste gases from burning this fuel shoot out of the back of the engine.

Go compare

A typical internal combustion or gas turbine engine is about 20 percent efficient. How does this compare with other devices we use? Electric motors are far more efficient. An electric motor can convert about 85 percent of the electricity it uses into movement. However, **incandescent light bulbs** are much less efficient. Over 90 percent of the electricity powering a light bulb is wasted as heat.

NOTICING THE PROBLEM

Air pollution was the first environmental problem linked to transportation to get noticed. In the 1950s, the UK government introduced a Clean Air Act to try to reduce air pollution. The act was aimed mainly at reducing the amount of soot coming from factories and coal fires. However, in 1960, investigators in the United States looked at the causes of smog in large cities such as Los Angeles. They found that much of the pollution was caused by gases from car exhausts. In 1963, the U.S. government passed its own Clean Air Act, aimed at trying to control the pollution from car exhausts. It was one of the first attempts to try to stop the environmental damage caused by cars and other transportation.

Today, environmental activists from Greenpeace protest against pollution. Oil can be extracted from tar sands like these in Canada, but it involves cutting down large areas of forest, and the process produces large amounts of carbon dioxide.

The environmental movement starts

The environmental movement was already quite strong in the United States by the time the Clean Air Act was passed. It began in the mid-1800s, when a few people began to object to the way that humans were damaging the natural environment. U.S. environmental pioneers, such as John Muir and George Perkins Marsh, were involved in establishing national parks, which are unspoiled wilderness areas that are protected to maintain natural habitats.

By the start of the 1960s, there were national parks in many countries. Environmentalists were mainly concerned with protecting natural areas and wildlife. Most people still knew very little about environmental damage or pollution of the air and water.

Then and Now
Muir and Marsh

John Muir and George Perkins Marsh both lived in the 1800s, but their ideas are still relevant today.

Muir was a naturalist who wanted to protect wilderness areas in the United States. He founded one of the first-ever environmental organizations, the Sierra Club. Its aim was to "explore, enjoy, and protect the wild places of Earth." He also helped to found Yosemite National Park. The modern science of **ecology** has shown that the animals and plants living in a habitat are interconnected in a complex web. Muir recognized this before ecology had been invented. He said, "When one tugs at a single thing in nature, he finds it attached to the rest of the world."

Marsh wrote one of the first books on ecology, called *Man and Nature*. He argued that cutting down forests would lead to erosion and degrading of the soil. This is just what has happened where areas of rain forest have been cut down.

A wider audience

During the 1960s, people became more aware of the effects of pollution, especially in the United States, as U.S. cities such as New York City and Los Angeles suffered from smog (see page 6). The Cuyahoga River in Ohio caught fire because there was so much pollution in the water.

In 1967, the *Torrey Canyon* oil tanker sank off the coast of Cornwall, England, causing one of the first major oil spills. A book called *Silent Spring*, by the U.S. biologist Rachel Carson, showed how a **pesticide** called DDT was poisoning wildlife in many parts of the world. *Silent Spring* became a best seller, and it made millions of people aware of how human actions could cause environmental problems.

Taking action

By the end of the 1960s, the environmental movement had grown very large. Earth Day protests in the United States showed just how many people were worried about pollution and the environment. The first Earth Day took place on April 22, 1970. Over 20 million Americans took part in demonstrations and marches across the country. College students went to lectures in gas masks to highlight the problems of air pollution. Students picked up litter from the streets, and some New York City streets were closed to all cars. Over a million people gathered for the Earth Day rally in Central Park in New York City.

Not all environmental protests have an impact. In 1996, many protesters in the United Kingdom tried to persuade planners to change the route of a bypass in Berkshire, England—but the road was built as planned.

The environmental protests were large, and they did have some effects on transportation. There were many protests in the United States and Europe against the building of large roads, and some road-building projects were abandoned. But it was another event, which had nothing to do with environmentalists, that led to the first real moves away from fossil fuels in transportation.

Then and Now
Different protests

Environmentalists supporting the first Earth Day were protesting about many different things. Many of their concerns were the same as those of environmentalists today. They wanted power stations to reduce the amounts of polluting gases they were pumping into the air. They wanted mining companies, oil producers, and chemical factories to stop dumping toxic waste materials that could poison the environment. They were worried about oil spills from large tankers and the loss of wilderness areas. But there was one big difference from environmental concerns today. There were no large protests against global warming. This was because, in the 1960s, the problem of global warming was only just being recognized.

Making an impact

Since the 1960s, environmentalists have been less successful in actually stopping road-building projects. However, environmental arguments do often influence the routes of roads and where airports are built. Today, any new road or airport needs an environmental assessment that shows how the road or building will affect the environment and how the negative impact can be kept to a minimum.

ENVIRONMENTALISM IN ACTION

The energy crisis

In the early 1970s, environmentalists protesting about transportation were concerned about the increasing numbers of cars on the road, the numbers of new roads being built, and the particulate emissions that caused smog. Few people concerned about the environment were worrying about reducing carbon dioxide emissions or reducing fossil fuel use.

Crude oil was the most important fossil fuel at the time. We relied on oil even more than we do today. So, when there was a problem with the oil supply in October 1973, it shook the world.

A political argument

The oil crisis was the result of a political argument between the United States and Arab countries in the Middle East. The Middle East countries are the biggest oil producers in the world. They are members of the Organization of Oil Exporting Countries (OPEC).

In 1973, the United States was supporting Israel in a war with the Middle Eastern countries Syria and Egypt. Because of this support, the Arab members of OPEC decided to stop selling oil to the United States. At the same time, they increased the price of oil to Europe, Japan, and other wealthy countries by 70 percent.

Shortages and rationing

The oil crisis quickly had serious effects—especially in the United States. The United States is a big oil producer, but it uses even more oil than it produces. In the 1970s, nearly all this oil came from the Middle East. Within a few days, there were lines at gasoline stations. By early 1974, 20 percent of U.S. gasoline stations had no fuel at all.

The U.S. government brought in rationing to try to avoid lines at the gasoline pumps. Cars with license plates that ended in an odd number could buy gasoline on odd-numbered days, while license plates with even numbers could only fill up on even-numbered days.

What is oil?

Crude oil is a liquid mixture of **hydrocarbons** that is found underground. The different parts of the crude oil mixture are separated in an oil refinery.

Crude oil is the most important fossil fuel. Gasoline, diesel, and aviation fuel are all extracted from oil. Fuel oil powers most of our electricity production and is a major heating fuel.

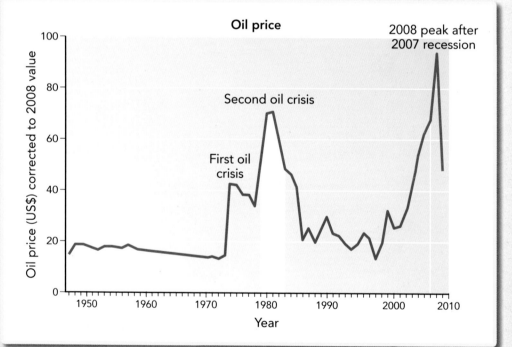

This shows changes in the average price of crude oil since 1947. The peaks in oil prices during the 1970s and 1980s were caused by oil crises, but the reasons for the huge spike in oil prices during 2008 are unclear.

Longer-lasting effects

After only a few months, the United States and Arab OPEC members sorted out their political problems, and the oil supply to the United States resumed. However, the crisis showed the oil-producing countries how powerful they were. Oil prices remained high for most of the 1970s, and there was a second oil crisis in 1979.

The high oil prices led the United States and other rich countries to look for ways to reduce their reliance on oil. When oil was cheap, many Americans drove large cars that used lots of fuel. These "gas-guzzlers" were replaced by smaller, more efficient vehicles. Governments also encouraged research into solar power, electric vehicles, and other renewable alternatives to oil. In Brazil, the government began making an alternative to gasoline from sugarcane (see page 33).

Then and Now
The CitiCar

In 1974, a U.S. company called Vanguard-Sebring produced an all-electric, two-seater car called the CitiCar. Its motor produced 3.5 horsepower, it had a top speed of 40 miles (64 kilometers) per hour, and it needed recharging after about 40 miles. It was light and did not rust. The CitiCars sold in the thousands, and Vanguard-Sebring became the sixth-biggest car manufacturer in the United States. However, as the oil crisis faded, the car lost popularity, and the company went out of business.

In 1974, the all-electric Vanguard-Sebring was one of the best-selling cars in the United States.

The impact of environmentalism

The oil crises of 1973 and 1979 probably did more than anything else to kick-start research into alternatives to fossil fuels. Environmental concerns were not the main reason behind decisions to build electric cars and develop solar power. However, environmentalism has had some impact. The research that began in the 1970s could have stopped once oil supplies were restored. But broader concerns about the environment meant that the research continued into the 21st century. The results of this research are an important part of much of today's "green" technology.

In recent years, a few all-electric cars have begun to appear. One example is the Nissan Leaf, which went on sale in the United States and Japan in 2010. The Leaf is a four-seater that looks and feels like any family car. The motor produces 110 horsepower, and the car has a top speed of 93 miles (150 kilometers) per hour. Because it uses an electric motor, the Leaf needs no gears. It can accelerate strongly at any speed, which makes it fun to drive. However, it has a maximum range of only 100 miles (160 kilometers) before it needs to be plugged into a standard electrical outlet for several hours to be recharged.

The Nissan Leaf is one of several electric cars to come onto the market in recent years.

SUSTAINABLE DEVELOPMENT

In the 1980s and 1990s, many people forgot about the oil scares of the 1970s, but scientists were finding more evidence of global warming and environmental damage.

In 1983, the United Nations set up the World Commission on Environment and Development to look at what could be done about the growing problems of the planet. The commission produced a report in 1987 called *Our Common Future*, or the Brundtland Report. It suggested practical ways in which we could reduce pollution and damage to the environment.

Our Common Future identified many environmental problems facing the world. The report concluded that the richer countries were using up Earth's resources more quickly than they could be replaced or renewed. What was needed was **sustainable** development.

Sustainable development: The aims

The world economy is currently based on economic development. This means that countries try to increase the amount of money they make from selling **goods** (things they make) and services (things they do, such as banking, nursing, or hairdressing).

Sustainable development takes a longer-term view of Earth and its resources. According to the Commission on Environment and Development: "Sustainable development is development that meets the needs of the present without compromising the ability of future generations to meet their own needs." Some of the ways to improve sustainability include recycling materials and using energy resources that are renewable, such as solar or wind power. But for transportation, one of the most important improvements has been making vehicles more efficient.

Government targets

In the years since the Brundtland Report, governments of countries around the world have begun to take the issue of climate change and global warming seriously. Today, most countries have targets for reducing their carbon emissions, with some hoping to reduce emissions by around 20 percent and others with goals of reductions of 50 percent or more. The emissions from transportation will certainly have to be reduced to help meet these targets.

An ice core is drilled in the Arctic. Scientists can use ice cores to get information about past climates, stretching back thousands of years. This kind of evidence has helped to show that human actions are changing the world climate.

Our Common Future

The main point of the Brundtland Report was that we are using up the planet's resources so quickly that the natural environment cannot recover and renew itself. The effects of this behavior will be felt by our children and grandchildren rather than by people living today. A quote from the Brundtland Report made this point very clearly:

"We borrow environmental capital from future generations with no intention or prospect of repaying. They may damn us for our spendthrift ways, but they can never collect on our debt to them. We act as we do because we can get away with it: future generations do not vote; they have no political or financial power; they cannot challenge our decisions."

Improved efficiency

Despite the findings of the Brundtland Report, we continue to use fossil fuels to power cars, trains, aircraft, and other vehicles. However, there has been one major improvement: most of the engines that power these vehicles are more efficient than they were in the 1980s.

We saw on page 12 that engines are not very efficient. They are not very good at turning the chemical energy from fuel into kinetic energy. Some of this inefficiency is "built in." It is not possible for an engine of this kind to be 100 percent efficient, even in theory. However, it has proved possible to make substantial improvements in engine efficiency.

The move to diesel

There have been many changes that have improved efficiency. One of the most important has been the shift to diesel cars. Diesel engines use nearly one-third less fuel than gasoline engines.

In the 1970s, diesels were dirty and noisy. They were used only in trucks. Today's diesel engines are quieter and more efficient. They are often turbocharged (see page 25), which gives them better power and acceleration. Modern diesel fuels are much cleaner than in the past. Also, filters fitted to the exhaust prevent soot and other particulates from escaping into the air.

All these improvements, plus their better fuel consumption, have made diesel cars increasingly popular. In 2011, sales of diesel cars in the United States rose 37 percent over the previous year.

Future developments: Six-stroke engines

Most gasoline and diesel engines today are four-stroke engines. This means that there is one power stroke (combustion) for every four piston strokes (down, up, down, up). However, several types of six-stroke engine are currently being developed. Early tests suggest they could be 40 percent more efficient than a similar four-stroke engine.

The BMW X6 is not a "green" car. It is heavy and powerful, with a large, 3-liter engine. However, the start–stop system and regenerative braking reduce fuel consumption and save battery power.

Other improvements

Many other improvements since the 1970s have helped to make car engines more efficient:

- *Fuel injection:* In the 1970s, most cars had carburetors, where fuel and air were mixed before they were sprayed into the cylinder. Today, fuel injection systems mix fuel and air more accurately without the need for a carburetor.

- *Turbos and superchargers:* Turbos and superchargers are types of fan that compress the air going into the engine cylinders. With compressed air, the explosion of the fuel gives more power. An engine with a turbocharger or supercharger can be smaller than a non-turbo version and produce the same power.

- *Start–stop system:* Energy is wasted when a car is stopped with the engine idling. Start–stop systems automatically stop the engine when it has been idling for a second or two, then start it up again when the driver presses the accelerator.

- *Regenerative braking:* When a car brakes, its kinetic energy is usually lost as heat in the brakes, through friction. With regenerative braking, some of the kinetic energy is used to power a generator. This means that braking charges the battery, rather than heating up the brake pads.

Better jets

The fuel efficiency of jet engines has improved even more than that of gasoline and diesel engines.

In the first jet engines (**turbojets**), all the air drawn in by the compressor went into the combustion chamber and came out of the engine as hot gas. Modern airline engines are known as "high-bypass" jets, because most of the air passes around the combustion chamber rather than going through it. The bypass air absorbs heat from the combustion chamber as it flows around it. This heat would otherwise be lost into the atmosphere. The jet of gas coming out of the back of the engine is a mix of warm bypass air with very hot combustion gases. A high-bypass jet gives more thrust (forward "push") than a turbojet of the same size.

Efficient turbofan engines work best in modern airliners, which spend most of their time cruising. Military jets are far less efficient, because they need to produce more thrust. To do this, less of the air going into the engine is bypassed around the combustion chamber. For sudden bursts of speed, military jets have an afterburner. This is a mechanism for burning fuel at high temperatures in the jet exhaust. Afterburners give a lot of thrust, but they are very inefficient.

Higher emissions

Transportation today is much more energy-efficient than in the 1970s. Despite this, the carbon emissions from cars and other vehicles are much greater now. There are two main reasons for this.

The first reason is that there are many more cars on the roads. In 1969, just before the oil crisis, there were around 217 million cars on the road. Today, the number has almost tripled, to around 600 million. Passenger air miles flown increased from around 12 billion in 1973 to over 800 billion in 2010.

The second reason is that we expect much more from cars today than we did in the past. In the 1970s, only top luxury cars had features such as power steering and air conditioning. Today, they will be included as standard on even a fairly basic family car. Safety standards are also much higher for modern cars, which must have features such as side-impact bars and crumple zones to protect the driver and passenger. These extra features make cars heavier and use extra energy.

Future directions

A new kind of turbofan developed by U.S. engine-makers Pratt & Whitney could make big reductions in carbon emissions from jet aircraft. In a normal turbofan engine, the large turbine that draws in air at the front of the engine turns at the same speed as the much smaller turbine that compresses the air going into the combustion chamber. However, it would be more efficient if the large turbine could turn at slower speeds and the small compressor could turn much faster. The Pratt & Whitney PurePower® engine is a new kind of engine called a geared turbofan. It has a gearbox between the large and small turbines, so that they can both turn at optimum speeds.

This is the Pratt & Whitney PurePower® engine. It is a shorter, lighter engine that can produce the same amount of power using 12 to 15 percent less fuel.

ENVIRONMENTALISM IN ACTION

Cutting down waste

In one particular way, cars have always been friendly to the environment. Most of the materials in them have always been recycled. A car or other vehicle contains large amounts of steel, some aluminum, lead, and other valuable metals. All these metals can be separated from each other, melted down, and used again. There is a huge worldwide industry involved in breaking up damaged vehicles and separating the different metals in them for recycling.

Scrap dealers buy used cars and break them up, because they can make money from selling the scrap metal. However, recycling also gives a big environmental advantage. A car or other vehicle is a complex piece of machinery that takes a lot of energy to make. More often than not, this energy comes from fossil fuels. If the materials from a car are recycled, we get some of this energy back. And every ton of steel or other metal reclaimed from a car saves having to dig up and extract a ton of metal from rock.

The more of a car that can be recycled, the more energy it saves. The easiest material to recycle is steel. However, the amount of steel in cars is decreasing. In the 1970s, about 87 percent of a car was steel. A modern car is only about 65 percent steel. Lighter materials, such as aluminum and plastics, have replaced some of the steel. Aluminum can be recycled, but plastics are difficult to reuse and usually end up in landfill.

Many manufacturers have tried to make more of their cars recyclable or **biodegradable**. Two kinds of material have been used instead of plastics. The first are materials that are made from recycled waste. Volkswagen, for example, is processing plastics, glass, textiles, and rubber from old cars and using them again.

The other approach is to make new kinds of plastic that are made from plant material instead of from oil. These kinds of **biomaterials** have two advantages. First, they are sustainable because new plants can be grown to replace those used to make plastics. Second, bioplastics are biodegradable. They break down into simple materials and are naturally recycled in the environment.

What's next?

Researchers have built the World F3rst, a car that shows just how much can be done toward making cars more environmentally friendly. It is a full-blown race car, with a top speed of 150 miles (240 kilometers) per hour, using sustainable materials.

Many parts of the car are made from biomaterials. The front spoiler is made from potato **starch**, and some other body parts are made from hemp and flax fibers. The steering wheel is a kind of plastic made from carrots. Other body parts are made from recycled materials. The engine runs on a **biofuel** (see page 30) made from waste chocolate, and it is lubricated by plant oils.

The World F3rst race car is the first ever race car to be built largely from sustainable materials.

GREENER FUELS

By the 1990s, scientists and environmentalists had put together a convincing argument to show that carbon dioxide emissions from burning fossil fuels were causing climate change. Governments began to take the problem seriously.

In 1992, more than 100 world leaders met in Rio de Janeiro, Brazil, for the first Earth Summit. Their aim was to address Earth's urgent environmental problems, particularly climate change. Many countries signed a treaty called the Framework Convention on Climate Change (FCCC). This was an agreement that countries would work together to keep greenhouse gases in the atmosphere down, and so avoid dangerous warming of the planet.

In 1997, at the second Earth Summit, 191 countries signed the Kyoto Protocol. This involved countries promising to reduce their carbon emissions to specific levels by 2012. The United States did not sign the protocol.

After 1997, governments began to look for ways to reduce their carbon emissions. One way to reduce emissions from transportation looked very promising. This was to replace fossil fuels with biofuels.

What are biofuels?

Fossil fuels are the remains of plants and animals that died millions of years ago. These remains were crushed and heated below ground for long periods. Eventually they formed oil, gas, or coal.

Living plants and animals have the same basic ingredients as fossil fuels. So, with some careful crushing and cooking, it should be possible to use plants or animal wastes to make fuels. Fuels made this way are called biofuels.

Big advantages

Biofuels have some big advantages over fossil fuels. First, they are a renewable energy source. If we make biofuel from sugarcane, for example, it is not a one-time process. We can grow a new batch of sugarcane every year. Another advantage is that biofuels can be made locally. Some countries are rich in fossil fuels, while others have hardly any. But any country can grow crops or use waste materials to make biofuels.

The biggest advantage of biofuels is that, in theory, they produce fewer carbon emissions than fossil fuels.

Biofuels in theory

Fossil fuels and biofuels produce similar amounts of carbon dioxide when they burn. So, how can a biofuel produce fewer emissions? To understand, we need to go back to when the biofuel crop is planted. Like any plant, the fuel crop makes its food by photosynthesis. In this process, the plant combines carbon dioxide and water, using light energy from the Sun, to make sugars. The sugars are used to fuel the plant's growth. So, all the time it is growing, the plant is absorbing carbon dioxide from the atmosphere and turning it into plant material.

When the biofuel crop burns, it emits carbon dioxide. However, the carbon emissions are offset by the carbon dioxide that the plant absorbed while it was growing.

Biofuels for aircraft

Researchers have recently begun tests on using biofuels in aircraft. The first test flights using biofuels were made in 2010. In 2011, the airline Lufthansa made the first commercial flights using biofuels. Many other airlines have recently begun to experiment with using biofuels.

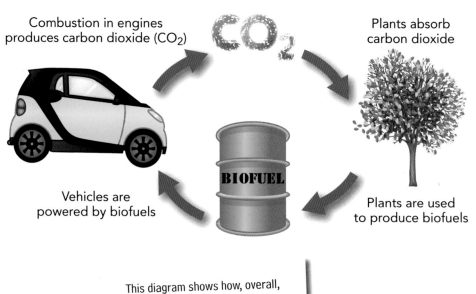

Combustion in engines produces carbon dioxide (CO_2)

Plants absorb carbon dioxide

Vehicles are powered by biofuels

BIOFUEL

Plants are used to produce biofuels

This diagram shows how, overall, biofuels recycle carbon dioxide.

Types of biofuel

There are several different types of biofuel.

Bioethanol: Bioethanol is alcohol made from plants. Alcohol burns in a similar way to gasoline, so gasoline engines can be modified fairly easily to use bioethanol. The two biggest bioethanol producers are the United States, which makes bioethanol from corn, and Brazil, where bioethanol is made from sugarcane.

Biodiesel: Biodiesel is made from plant oils or animal fats. It can be used as a replacement for diesel fuel with minimal changes to the engine. At the moment, most biodiesel is made from soybean oil, palm oil, or rapeseed oil. However, some biodiesel plants can use different kinds of oils and fats, such as waste animal fat from **slaughterhouses**.

In Linköping, Sweden, the local train and a fleet of buses run on biogas. This biofuel is made from animal waste from local slaughterhouses.

Biogas: Biogas is gas produced by **fermenting** animal wastes or other organic material. In fermentation, the waste material is kept warm in a closed container. Bacteria and other microbes "eat" the waste, and biogas is produced. Biogas is a mixture of methane (natural gas) with other gases. The methane can be purified and used as a transportation fuel, but the vehicles have to be built in a special way to run on gas.

Two types of biofuel

The same biofuel produced in different ways can produce very different carbon emissions.

In the 1970s, Brazil began making bioethanol from sugarcane. All the fuel for cars sold in Brazil since 1976 has been a mixture of bioethanol and gasoline. The cars have "flexfuel" engines that are designed to run on a mixture of the two fuels.

Bioethanol production in Brazil is very efficient. Sugarcane grows without the need for fertilizers or other chemicals. It produces a large amount of biofuel per acre of land on which it is grown, and the waste from processing (a material called bagasse) can be used as a heating fuel. Bioethanol produced this way has carbon emissions that are 61 percent lower than the emissions from fossil fuels.

The United States is the world's biggest bioethanol producer. Bioethanol in the United States is made from corn, which is planted and harvested by machines. Fertilizers are used to improve yields. The farm machinery is powered by fossil fuels, and the process of making fertilizers produces carbon emissions. This means that the overall savings in carbon emissions are much smaller than for Brazilian bioethanol. According to the U.S. Department of Energy, bioethanol made from corn produces carbon emissions that are about 20 percent lower than the emissions from fossil fuels.

Biofuel problems

Biofuels seem like a perfect replacement for fossil fuels. They absorb carbon dioxide while they are growing, then they give it out again when they burn. In theory, they should be carbon neutral, meaning they offset any carbon emissions they give off.

However, many environmentalists are opposed to replacing fossil fuels with biofuels. This is because in practice, using biofuels is not as straightforward as it seems in theory.

Different in practice

In most cases, growing biofuels produces carbon emissions. Farmers usually use machines to plant the crops and to harvest them. They may also use fertilizers, pesticides, and irrigation (extra watering systems) to get a good crop. All these processes produce carbon emissions.

A second problem is that biofuels are often grown on land that would otherwise be used for food crops. Some biofuel crops, such as corn and sugarcane, are grown as food crops in addition to being used for biofuels. This becomes a problem if we want to produce large amounts of biofuels. It will be an even bigger problem as the world population grows, because more people need more food. If we want to grow large amounts of biofuels, there will not be enough fertile land available for growing both food and fuel.

Economic problems

Producing biofuels has had some consequences that perhaps no one expected. Biofuel crops are valuable. They often sell for more money than food crops. Farmers often choose to grow biofuels to make money, not because they are good for the environment. Some farmers have removed food crops and planted biofuel crops instead. Others have cleared important habitats such as rain forest to grow biofuel crops. In such cases, the benefits of the biofuels are far outweighed by the damage caused to the environment.

Better than diesel

Biodiesel is in many ways a better fuel than diesel oil. It burns more readily than modern diesel fuel, which makes the engine more efficient. It also produces fewer particulates (less soot). Biodiesel is less **corrosive** than normal diesel fuel. This reduces wear and tear on fuel systems.

Second and third generation

Scientists are working on new kinds of biofuel that avoid the problems of the current biofuels. "Second generation" biofuels will be made from crops such as trees and grasses that can grow on land not suitable for growing food. The biofuel will be made from all of the plant, not just from starch or plant oils. It is possible to make these kinds of biofuels today, but it is much more expensive than biofuel made from crops such as corn or soybeans.

Biofuels can also be made from microscopic, plant-like **algae**. Some kinds of algae naturally produce oils. If this oil production can be increased enough, they could become a very useful source of biofuels.

Another possibility is to make biofuel from seaweed. Seaweed grows very quickly, and "seaweed farms" would not take up land that could be used to grow food.

An experimental farm in France grows algae in large tanks. The algae contain oils that can be extracted and used as biofuel.

ELECTRICS AND HYBRIDS

Since 1997, many countries have been trying to reduce their carbon emissions to meet their Kyoto Protocol targets. To reduce carbon emissions from transportation, governments have tried to make agreements with car manufacturers.

Some car manufacturers have gotten close to the emissions targets set for 2012. However, many others have not. Many environmental campaigners think we need new, ambitious targets if we are going to slow down global warming. The group Transportation and Environment, for example, suggests we should reduce average car emissions to 2.8 ounces per mile (80 grams per kilometer) by 2020. It will be very difficult to meet these suggested emissions targets with conventional cars. Could electric vehicles be the answer?

How much do they save?

Electric vehicles do not directly produce any carbon emissions. Most electric vehicles may have batteries to provide electric power. These batteries have to be recharged, and this is usually done from standard electrical outlets. Most of our electricity comes from power stations burning fossil fuels. So, a large amount of the electricity used to power electric vehicles comes from fossil fuels.

However, a vehicle running on electricity does have some advantages over a vehicle with an internal combustion engine:

- Electric vehicles are quieter than conventional ones.

- Electric vehicles do not need gears.

- Electric motors do not produce emissions directly, so they reduce pollution in busy towns and cities.

- A fossil fuel power station can produce electricity more efficiently than a vehicle engine could use the same fuel. For example, a conventional power station is about 36 to 38 percent efficient. A combined-cycle power station, which uses gas and steam turbines, can turn 50 to 60 percent of its fuel into electricity. An average car engine is only about 20 percent efficient.

- Not all power stations use fossil fuels. Many countries are moving toward hydroelectric systems (using water power) and other renewable sources.

Shorter range

Perhaps the main disadvantage of battery-powered electric vehicles is that, at the moment, they cannot travel as far on a single charge as an engine-powered vehicle can go on a full tank of gasoline or diesel. A battery-powered car, for example, has a range of about 100 miles (160 kilometers) on a single charge, while a conventional car might travel 500 miles (804 kilometers) on a full tank.

This is the battery compartment of a modern electric car. This model is the Peugeot iOn.

Then and Now
Electric vehicles

Electric vehicles are not a new invention. From the 1880s until the early 1900s, electric cars were as popular as those with gasoline or diesel engines. They were much quieter and less smelly than early internal combustion cars. From 1898 until 1902, electric cars held the world land speed record. The holder for most of this time was a car called *Le Jamais Contente*, which reached 65.8 miles (105.9 kilometers) per hour. In the early 1900s, gasoline became much cheaper, and electric cars fell out of fashion. But many trains, and also vehicles such as forklifts, are still powered by electricity today.

Slow charging

The big disadvantage of a modern electric vehicle is the time taken to refuel. You can fill up a car fuel tank in a few minutes, but recharging an electric vehicle takes several hours. At the moment, it is also more difficult to recharge an electric vehicle, because there are many gasoline stations but very few recharging stations.

In recent years, light, powerful batteries have been developed for devices such as laptops and cell phones. The advances in battery technology have improved batteries for electric cars. But even with these improvements, electric cars are not as cheap and convenient as conventional ones.

Fuel cells and hybrids

Two alternatives to straight battery power are **fuel cells** and **hybrids**. Fuel cells are "batteries" that run on fuel and do not need recharging. A fuel cell can combine hydrogen fuel with oxygen from the air to make electricity. The only waste product from this reaction is water. Cars that run on fuel cells have electric motors, but they use fuel like a conventional car. However, at the moment, fuel cells are extremely expensive to make and cannot compete with batteries.

Hybrids are cars powered by a combination of an electric motor and a small IC engine. In most hybrids on the road today, the main power comes from the IC engine. When extra power is needed (for example, when accelerating hard), the electric motor kicks in. The car therefore has the same power as a conventional car with a bigger engine.

Many car manufacturers produce hybrid cars. In general, they have better fuel consumption than similar cars with only IC engines. However, they are more complex mechanically, so they are more expensive to build and to maintain.

Energy from hydrogen?

A fuel cell "burns" hydrogen and oxygen together to produce electricity and water. If the wastewater is collected, it can be converted back to hydrogen and oxygen (this process needs energy). In theory, it would be possible to build a whole energy system on burning hydrogen to get energy and water, then converting the water back to hydrogen fuel. However, there are many problems connected with producing, storing, and using hydrogen.

Efficient batteries

Researchers at the Massachusetts Institute of Technology may have found an answer to the biggest problem with electric cars—the time they take to charge. Professor Gerbrand Ceder and student Byoungwoo Kang have discovered that just changing the way of making the material used in the batteries in electric cars can massively reduce charging times. A battery made this way recharges in seconds or minutes, rather than minutes or hours.

This special cutaway engine built in 2006 shows the electric motor (right) and gasoline engine (left) under the hood of a hybrid car.

RETHINKING LIFESTYLES

Designing more efficient engines, using more biofuels, and developing better electric or hybrid vehicles will help to reduce carbon emissions. However, as we have seen, environmentalists have shown that all these technological fixes have problems. They argue that we need to rethink our whole attitude toward the way we travel.

Congestion and pollution

The aim of a transportation system is to move people and goods from place to place as quickly and easily as possible. In many of the world's biggest cities, this just does not happen. There are regular traffic jams at rush hour, and an accident or other problem can lead to massive delays.

One of the main reasons for this is that stores, offices, and other businesses are concentrated in the center of cities. Millions of people have to travel into and out of the center each day to get to work. In many places, people travel to and from the city in their cars because public transportation is unreliable or too expensive. Many parents also use cars to take their children to school.

Long-distance travel

Another big use of transportation is to move food and other goods around the world. A U.S. study showed that on average, fresh produce such as fruits and vegetables travels almost 1,500 "food miles" (2,400 kilometers) from where it is grown to where it is eventually sold. The transportation for these foods uses large amounts of energy and produces tons of carbon emissions. Many foods have to be refrigerated in transit in order to stay fresh, and this adds to the energy used during transportation.

Environmentalists have led a campaign to persuade people to buy local produce from farmers' markets whenever possible. However, it is not always possible to buy some products locally—and in some cases food grown in developing countries, where no machinery or chemicals are used, actually has lower overall carbon emissions than locally grown food.

Crawling cars

The speed limit in many cities is around 30 miles (48 kilometers) per hour. However, congestion in many cities means that cars and other vehicles travel much more slowly than the limit. In the business district of New York City, the average speed of traffic is just 9.5 miles (15 kilometers) per hour. The average speed of motor vehicles in Indian cities is about the same. At these speeds, it could actually be quicker to travel by bicycle!

In 1930 (upper photo), the streets of the city of Mumbai, India, were virtually free of traffic. By 2009 (lower photo), traffic levels had increased massively.

Then and Now
India and China

More than one-third of the world's population lives in the Asian countries of India and China. Since 1990, the number of cars in these two countries has skyrocketed. In 2005, India had three times as many cars as in 1990, while in China there were ten times more cars. In many cities, the increase has caused air pollution, traffic congestion, noise, accidents, parking problems, and increased energy use.

Smarter planning

Reorganizing the transportation network of a city is a big job. However, some cities have found ways to reduce the amount of traveling people have to do (see the case study on pages 44–47).

One way to bring down the energy costs of transportation would be to reduce the distances people travel to work or to school. The best way to do this would be to reorganize our cities. Complete reorganization would be difficult, but it may be possible to use planning laws to ensure a mix of businesses and housing spread across a city, instead of having the businesses concentrated in the center.

Fewer cars

If vehicles were used more efficiently, it would reduce the amount of energy use. For example, there is often only one person traveling in a car—the driver. One way to avoid this is carpooling, in which people who are traveling the same route share a car. Carpooling is most often used for regular journeys, such as school trips or going to and from work. However, it is also possible to use carpooling for longer trips.

Using more public transportation reduces the numbers of private cars on the road and so reduces energy use. Planners in many cities have tried many ways to do this. One of the simplest is to make sure that bus and train services are regular, cheap, and do not get held up in traffic. Special bus lanes are often created. Many cities have park-and-ride programs, in which drivers leave their cars in parking lots on the edge of a city, then travel into town on public transportation.

One program for reducing the traffic in a city center is "congestion charging." Private vehicles have to pay to drive in the most congested parts of a city. Congestion charging has been introduced in cities such as London, where many people have switched to public transportation in order to avoid paying the fee.

Perhaps one of the best ways to reduce the energy costs of transportation is not to use motor vehicles at all. Over half of all car journeys are less than 5 miles (8 kilometers). Trips of this length could be done on a bicycle.

Personal rapid transit

Personal rapid transit (PRT) is an experimental kind of transportation with many of the advantages of a car, but the energy savings of public transportation. A PRT system has small, lightweight vehicles controlled by computer that run on fixed tracks. Passengers board at set stations, but generally they will not have to wait; the car will already be waiting. Unlike a bus, it can go directly to the passenger's destination without stopping on the way. A few small PRT systems have already been built at places like airports. However, more work needs to be done before a large PRT network can be created.

Cellular city design

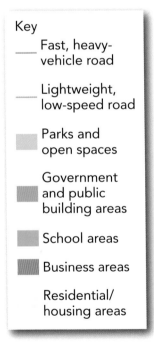

Key

____ Fast, heavy-vehicle road

____ Lightweight, low-speed road

Parks and open spaces

Government and public building areas

School areas

Business areas

Residential/ housing areas

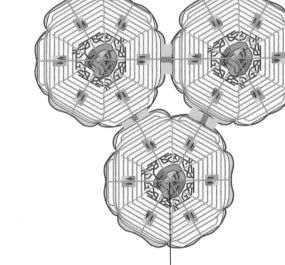

Hub, with schools, businesses, and government buildings

This plan shows how towns and cities could be reorganized to cut transportation costs. It consists of a series of "cells," each with a central business and government center. Fast roads carrying heavy traffic radiate out from the center, while slower, lighter traffic goes on roads connecting these radiating roads.

ENVIRONMENTALISM IN ACTION

Two traffic solutions

Two cities, one in Brazil in South America and one in the United States, have designed very different solutions to their transportation problems.

Curitiba, Brazil

In the 1960s, the city of Curitiba, Brazil, was growing fast, causing many problems. There was traffic chaos and pollution. Many poor people lived in slums where there was no water, electricity, or drains. The city needed a plan for improvement. The council decided to hold a competition to find ways to solve the city's problems. A group of architects was given the job of turning the best ideas from the competition into workable plans.

At the heart of the improvement plan was a new transportation network. Five major roads were built radiating out from the city center, like the spokes of a wheel. Each road has three parts. On one side, the traffic moves toward the city center; on the other side, it moves outward. Between the two is a two-way road that can be used only by the city's rapid transit system. This is a fleet of buses that can each carry 270 people.

A rapid bus stops at a station of the Bus Rapid Transit (BRT) system in Curitiba, Brazil.

The buses run every few minutes. The bus stops are long, tubular shelters where people can board very quickly. The fare is the same from any part of the city. The rapid transit buses stop on the edge of the city center, because only pedestrians are allowed in the center itself. In addition to the rapid transit buses, there are local buses that operate in the areas between the radiating "spokes."

Because the bus services in the city are so good, 85 percent of people use public transportation to travel around the city. This means that other traffic on the roads is much lighter than in other cities. The large rapid transit buses use far less fuel per passenger than private cars, so the transportation system produces fewer carbon emissions. Fuel use is 30 percent less than in other, similar Brazilian cities.

A green success

Curitiba is a great example of how planning can benefit everyone. It has a superb transportation system, but some areas in the center are closed to traffic, to make pleasant pedestrian areas. There are many parks and other green spaces and an excellent waste recycling system. In 2007, Curitiba was voted one of the greenest cities in the world.

The Curitiba city plan was a "big idea" for change that really worked. But big ideas do not always turn out so well…

Other environmental initiatives

The transportation system is not the only way in which planning in Curitiba is environmentally friendly. Some areas in the city have been protected from future development and have been turned into parks. Curitiba also set up a major recycling system well before it was used in other cities, recycling organic waste, plastic, glass, and metal.

Boston, Massachusetts

In the early 1970s, the city of Boston, Massachusetts, had big traffic problems. The center of the city was split in two by a six-lane raised expressway. The road was old and needed replacing. It was always congested, because traffic going from north to south and from east to west had to use the same stretch of road. The constant traffic produced large amounts of noise and air pollution in the city center.

Boston's governor and the head of transportation came up with a plan to replace the expressway with a tunnel 3.5 miles (5.6 kilometers) long right under the city center. The tunnel was just one part of "The Big Dig"—a huge engineering project that also involved building a new bridge and two underwater tunnels.

The Big Dig

The Big Dig was a very expensive project and was plagued with problems. There were leaks in the underwater tunnels and problems with the concrete being used. Four workers were killed in construction accidents. The project took over 20 years to complete and cost at least $15 billion. It will take the city until at least 2038 to pay off these costs.

When the Big Dig was completed in 2006, traffic flowed much more freely through the city. The central tunnel greatly reduced above-ground traffic in the city center, and the area where the expressway had been became parkland. As a result, the center of Boston became a more pleasant place.

A tale of two cities

Although it has reduced traffic congestion, the Big Dig has not reduced the overall amount of traffic through the city—and it has not cut down on carbon emissions or fossil fuel use. By contrast, the transportation system in Curitiba has produced real reductions in carbon emissions.

Environmental campaigners see the Big Dig as a planning failure. The program cost much more than was originally planned. This is mainly because it was a huge, complicated project that led to many mistakes and accidents. The transportation system built in Curitiba was much more straightforward, so it cost far less.

Most of the environmentally friendly parts of the original Big Dig plan were dropped. A rail link between the north and south parts of the city, which would have greatly reduced car use, was not built. Many parks, footpaths, cycle tracks, and pedestrian bridges were not completed. In Curitiba, "green" ideas were at the center of the plans for the city.

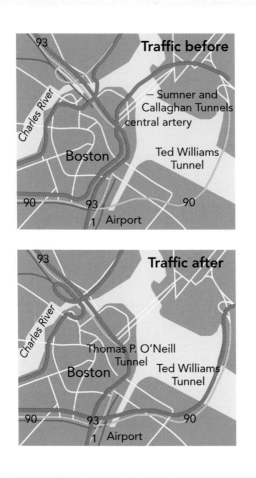

These maps show how the Big Dig changed roads in central Boston. Traffic traveling from east to west has been diverted out of the city center on Route 90, while north-to-south traffic on Route 93 now travels under the city center in the Thomas P. O'Neill Tunnel.

Signposts for the future

Since the 1970s, environmentalists, governments, and businesses across the world have tried to reduce carbon emissions and find alternatives to fossil fuels. But progress has been slow. For example, the first experiments with electric cars happened in the 19th century, but electric cars are still a tiny minority of overall car sales. So, what will happen in the future?

Do we need cars?

Some environmentalists think that the only way we will solve our transportation problems is to give up cars altogether. This seems unlikely to happen in the near future. People can do things in cars that would be much more difficult using other forms of transportation. They can go on a trip when they like, take far more luggage than they could carry on public transportation, and drive directly to their destination without having to stop at other places on the way. However, we have seen that with careful planning, it is possible to create cities where people do not have to travel far to get to work or to go shopping. Good public transportation, pleasant footpaths, and safe cycle routes can also help to reduce the need for cars.

Future power

Cars are unlikely to disappear in the near future. However, the way they are powered may change. They may use third-generation biofuels made from algae or seaweed, or they might run on batteries. Eventually, cars could be part of an economy in which hydrogen-powered fuel cells produce water as waste that is then turned back into hydrogen using solar power. We will need to consider all these new kinds of power (and other new ones) to replace fossil fuels.

Saving energy

Cars are very heavy compared to the people they carry. The average U.S. car weighs about 4,400 pounds (2,000 kilograms). Even with four people on board, 86 percent of the car's fuel is used to move the car itself. If we made cars smaller and lighter, this would produce big energy savings. Until recently, studies suggested that smaller, lighter cars were not as safe as large, heavy cars. However, more recent studies have shown that they are just as safe. So, cars in the future are likely to be lighter.

Cars, trains, and other vehicles are expensive to manufacture in terms of price, but also in terms of energy. One way to retrieve some of this energy is to recycle the vehicle parts. The interiors of these railroad cars are made from 97 percent recyclable materials.

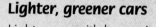

Lighter, greener cars

Lighter cars with low emissions look set to become a reality within a few years. The German manufacturer Audi is building an affordable, compact car with an aluminum body that keeps the weight down. Another German manufacturer, BMW, is developing a range of electric and hybrid cars with carbon-fiber bodies. In the United States, engineers at the Massachusetts Institute of Technology have designed a small, two-seater city car that weighs less than 2,200 pounds (1,000 kilograms) and can "fold up" to fit into a space of only 5 feet (1.5 meters) in length.

Powering ships and boats

Many of the advances in technology that have been developed for cars could also work for ships and boats. Boat engines could, for example, use biofuels in the same way that car engines can.

One development that is promising for powering ships is pod propulsion. Instead of being connected to the ship's engines by long shafts, the propellers are in "pods" slung below the hull. Pod systems can be built so that the whole unit can turn to point the propeller in a different direction. This means that the ship can steer using the pod units and does not need a rudder.

Propellers on pods below the hull give better streamlining, which saves energy. Having no rudder also reduces **drag** and saves more energy.

Using less energy on water

Land vehicles only have to move through air, which offers a lot less resistance than water. Boats in the future may use ideas currently being researched that aim to cut the drag of a boat hull by pumping air underneath it. Air cavity system (ACS) boats have a wedge-shaped cavity in the boat hull that is designed to trap air pumped into it. The air acts as a lubricating layer between the boat and the water. In experimental boats, ACS has cut drag by between 15 and 40 percent. ACS could allow future boats to travel at speeds of up to 50 knots (58 miles per hour) without huge rises in fuel consumption.

In some pod systems, the propellers are driven by an electric motor in the pod. Engines on board the ship generate the electricity. This system is more efficient than driving the propellers directly by using engines.

Future air transportation

Until recently, the main improvement in aircraft carbon emissions came from improvements in engine design (see page 27). However, the first airliners to use biofuel flew in 2011 (see page 31), and many future aircraft will probably run at least partly on biofuel.

There are many ideas for powering aircraft further into the future. There are several kinds of hybrid aircraft being developed. Some, like road hybrids, are conventional aircraft that have both an internal combustion engine and an electric motor. But the Lockheed-Martin P-791 is another kind of hybrid—a hybrid airship. It is heavier than air, so it does not actually float, but it takes off and lands like an aircraft. However, the aircraft includes three giant cells filled with the very light gas helium, like an airship. This makes the aircraft very buoyant and means it needs far less fuel to fly. Hybrids like this could stay airborne for many weeks and carry large loads.

Wind power

Ships in the future may use wind power to reduce fuel use. In 2008, the cargo ship MS *Beluga* made a two-week trip from Germany to Venezuela using a giant kite to help it along. The kite is similar to the parafoils used by kite surfers, but much bigger—about the area of a football field. On days when the wind is strong enough, the kite can reduce a ship's fuel consumption by an average of 10 to 15 percent.

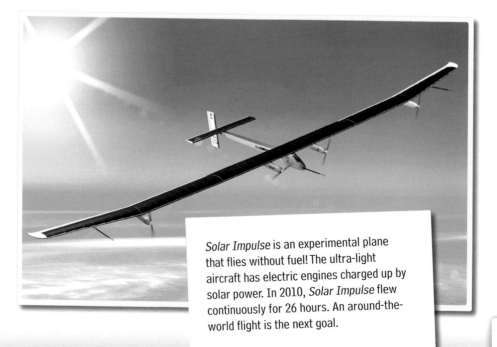

Solar Impulse is an experimental plane that flies without fuel! The ultra-light aircraft has electric engines charged up by solar power. In 2010, *Solar Impulse* flew continuously for 26 hours. An around-the-world flight is the next goal.

ENVIRONMENTALISM IN ACTION

A city for tomorrow?

Masdar is a new city being built in the desert, close to the city of Abu Dhabi. The whole city is an experiment in green planning and technology. The aim of the project is to use 50 percent less energy than in a conventional city of a similar size. When completed in 2025, Masdar will be home to about 50,000 people.

The layout and design of Masdar aim to make it comfortable to live in the buildings and walk the streets, even when the Sun is burning down on the desert. The buildings are close together and the streets are narrow, with overhanging roofs to provide shade. The whole city is walled, which provides more protection from the desert heat. The design is good for walking, but perhaps not so good for other kinds of transportation.

No internal combustion cars will be allowed in Masdar. All vehicles within the city will be electric. The electricity will come mainly from solar power stations in the desert close to the city, so the carbon emissions due to transportation will be very low.

This is an artist's impression of how Masdar will look from the air once it is finished.

In the original plan for Masdar, the city's transportation network was going to be below ground. A PRT system (see page 43) using 3,000 driverless cars was designed to be a kind of green taxi service that would deliver customers directly to their destination, 24 hours per day. A pilot project using 16 cars worked well and is still operating. However, the cost of the complete system was too high, so the idea has been dropped. Instead, transportation will consist of electric buses and cars, plus two railroad networks running from Abu Dhabi to the center of Masdar.

Although Masdar's transportation system will not be as futuristic as originally planned, the design of the city still points to the future. People visiting Masdar will arrive in high-speed transportation (such as trains) or conventional cars. In the city itself, there will be a different transportation system that produces no pollution and little noise. This will greatly reduce carbon emissions and keep the air in Masdar fresh.

Masdar facts

Where: Abu Dhabi, United Arab Emirates

Area: 2.3 square miles (6 square kilometers)

Population (expected): 45,000–50,000

Aim: To build a sustainable city relying entirely on renewable energy that uses only half the energy of a normal city of similar size

Project begun: 2006

Completion (expected): 2025

Cost (estimated): $19 billion

Designers: Norman Foster & Partners

Owners: Abu Dhabi Future Energy Company

"Only use energy when you have exhausted design."

Motto of architects from Norman Foster & Partners

ENVIRONMENTALISM IN ACTION

Testing new ideas

When scientists and engineers come up with new ideas, they have to find ways to test them in the real world. One way of doing this is through challenge events.

World Solar Challenge

The World Solar Challenge is a test of speed and endurance for cars powered entirely by the Sun. The Challenge is a race across the center of Australia, from Darwin in the north to Adelaide in the south. The total distance is about 1,860 miles (3,000 kilometers). Most entries are cars built at colleges. The cars are driven by electric motors, and the upper surface is covered with solar cells to provide the electricity. The cells are also used to charge the car's batteries.

In 2005, the winning car, *Nuna 3*, averaged a scorching 64 miles (103 kilometers) per hour. This was the fastest Solar Challenge car to date.

These Japanese winners are celebrating victory at the finishing line of the 2010 World Solar Challenge with their solar car, Tokai Challenge.

Shell Eco-Marathon

Three Shell Eco-Marathons are held each year in Europe, the United States, and Asia. The idea is not to see who can go the fastest, but rather who can go the farthest on 1 liter (a quarter of a gallon) of fuel, or on 1 kilowatt-hour of electricity.

The record for the most fuel-efficient car of all was set in 2005 by *PAC Car II*, designed and built by Team ETH from Switzerland. *Pac Car II* weighed only 64 pounds (29 kilograms). It was powered by a fuel cell that ran on hydrogen. In the 2005 race, it clocked a fuel consumption of 3,346 miles (5,385 kilometers) per liter of fuel. The car could almost drive all the way from Chicago to Los Angeles and back without a refill!

Car design

The cars taking part in the World Solar Challenge and the Shell Eco-Marathon are not practical. In most, there is only room for the driver, who has to lie almost flat and has a very limited view. But to win the challenges, design teams push the cars and materials to the limits.

Solar speed

The very first World Solar Challenge race in 1987 was won by a solar-powered car called *Sunraycer*, entered by a team from the U.S. car-maker General Motors. *Sunraycer* was much faster than the other cars in the race. It arrived in Adelaide two days before the second-place car! It also set a speed record of 75.276 miles (121.145 kilometers) per hour for a car powered only by the Sun (without batteries).

Sunraycer's speed record stood for 23 years. It was broken in 2011 by a car called *Sunswift IV*, or "*IVy*" for short. *IVy* was built by a team of students and employees from the University of New South Wales in Sydney, Australia. In January 2011, *IVy* reached a new world record speed of 88.5 miles (142.5 kilometers) per hour. This was over 13 miles (21 kilometers) per hour faster than *Sunraycer*.

WHAT HAVE WE LEARNED?

Since the 1960s, environmentalism has grown into a worldwide movement. By the 1990s, the impact of environmentalism led to the setting up of the United Nations Earth Summits and targets for reducing carbon emissions. However, the impact of environmentalism on our transportation systems has been limited.

In most countries, the main focus is on trying to make cars more environmentally friendly. This makes sense, because cars produce more emissions than any other form of transportation. However, environmentalists believe that this will not produce large reductions in carbon emissions. Even if we do improve the carbon emissions of cars, they will still use more energy than public transportation, bicycles, or walking. In this area, the environmental point of view has not had a strong impact.

Sustainable transportation

For truly sustainable transportation systems, environmentalists argue, we need to change our attitudes toward travel and transportation. We need to reorganize our lifestyles so that we live closer to where we work and shop. We need to improve our public transportation systems so that we use private vehicles far less. Future PRT electric-vehicle networks could provide a public transportation system with many of the advantages of private cars.

Keeping things moving

The arguments of environmentalists have had less impact on transportation than they have had in other areas, such as energy production. However, environmental arguments do have important effects. Changes to our transportation systems involve difficult decisions that are often unpopular. For that reason, politicians and governments often avoid or delay making these kinds of difficult decisions. However, as was found with congestion charging in the city of London (see page 42), these kinds of decisions can produce real benefits in the longer term. Environmentalists can help to keep the focus on why such changes are important.

The need to change our attitudes to transportation has become urgent. In 1990, the total world carbon emissions were about 24,000 tons. If we continue as we are, then by 2025 emissions will have reached almost 41,000 tons. Yet scientists believe that we need to reduce emissions well below 1990 levels by 2050 to prevent serious global environmental damage. We do not have much time.

The best sustainable transportation of all is a bike! These bicycle taxis operating in Sydney, Australia, also have a small electric motor to help get them up hills.

Discussion panel: Will it happen?

The basic problem is simple: we need to change our transportation systems, to use fossil fuels less, and to reduce carbon emissions. We have known about the problem for around 40 years. We know of many ways to reduce energy use and we now have the technology that could partly replace fossil fuels, and yet we have made very little progress toward developing sustainable transportation. Environmentalists have done an excellent job of alerting the world to the dangers of pollution and global warming, but the decisions that will really change things for the better have to be made by politicians from different countries working together. Will governments manage to do this before it is too late? The answer is in the balance.

TIMELINE

1820 The world population reaches 1 billion.

1839 The first crude fuel cell is developed by Welsh scientist William Grove.

1864 George Perkins Marsh publishes his book *Man and Nature*.

1885 John Stanley begins selling the Rover safety bicycle—the first modern bicycle.

1890 The work of John Muir helps to establish the Yosemite and Sequoia National Parks in California.

1899 Belgian Camille Jenatzy's electric car, *La Jamais Contente*, becomes the fastest car in the world. It travels at nearly 66 miles (106 kilometers) per hour.

1900 At the World's Fair, Rudolf Diesel runs his engine on pure peanut oil.
Belgian car manufacturer Pieper introduces a car powered by a combination of a small gasoline engine and an electric motor. This is one of the first hybrid car designs.

1921 Thomas Midgley Jr. discovers that a chemical containing lead works well to stop "knocking" (mistimed explosions) in gasoline engines. His invention is very successful, but it causes lead pollution in the atmosphere for 50 years or more.

1930 The world population reaches 2 billion.

1930s–1950s British inventor Francis Thomas Bacon develops the first practical fuel cell.

1939 The Shell Eco-Marathon starts out as a bet between scientists as to who can get the most miles per gallon from a car.

1952–1954 Smog problems in London, New York, and Los Angeles alert people to the dangers of air pollution.

1956 The Clean Air Act is introduced in the United Kingdom to reduce pollution from fires and smoke.

1958 Mauna Loa Observatory in Hawaii begins monitoring the levels of carbon dioxide in the atmosphere. Over time, the data shows a clear rise in carbon dioxide levels.

1962 Rachel Carson's book *Silent Spring* is published.

1963 The first of a series of Clean Air Acts in the United States that are designed to reduce pollution from cars as well as fires.

1968 Curitiba, Brazil, begins its "Master Plan" to reorganize the transportation system.

1969 The Cuyahoga River in Ohio catches fire because there is so much pollution in the water.

1970 The first Earth Day events are held across the United States.

1973 Brazil begins making bioethanol from sugarcane. Mass production of biofuel cars begins in 1979.
The first oil crisis occurs as oil prices rise steeply.

1974 The world population reaches 4 billion.

1987 The World Solar Challenge race across Australia is run for the first time. It offers a showcase for solar-powered cars.
The Brundtland Report, *Our Common Future*, talks about sustainable development.

1991 The Boston Big Dig begins.

1992 The UN Earth Summit is held in Rio de Janeiro, Brazil, from June 3 to 14.

1999 The world population reaches 6 billion.

2006 The first airline flight that is fueled by biofuel.

2008 Pratt & Whitney produce the Pratt & Whitney PurePower® engine, their first geared turbofan engine.

2010 The solar-powered aircraft *Solar Impulse* flies for over 26 hours powered only by sunlight.

2011 The world population reaches 7 billion.

GLOSSARY

acid rain rain caused by air pollution that damages forests and harms wildlife in rivers and lakes

algae plant-like living things found in all kinds of water. Algae range in size from microscopic organisms to huge seaweed.

biodegradable can be broken down in the environment into very simple chemicals

biofuel fuel made either from plant materials or animal waste

biomaterial plastic or other synthetic material made from plants

climate change shift in weather patterns, frequency of extreme weather events, and average temperatures caused by global warming

congestion road blockage caused by too much traffic

corrosive causing damage by a chemical process when in contact with other materials

drag resistance to flow

ecology area of science that studies the interactions between living things and their environment

efficient produces an amount of work that is close to the amount of energy put into it. Most engines can turn only about 25 percent of the energy in the fuel into useful work.

emission production and release of gas

fermenting turning a liquid into alcohol

fossil fuel naturally occurring fuel, usually found below ground or under the seabed, that takes millions of years to form. Coal, crude oil, and natural gas are the three major fossil fuels.

fuel cell device that uses hydrogen or a similar fuel, plus oxygen from the air, to produce electricity directly

global warming gradual rise in Earth's average temperature caused by an increase in greenhouse gases in the atmosphere

goods things that people manufacture (make) and sell

greenhouse gas gas that stores heat in the atmosphere. Carbon dioxide and methane are examples of greenhouse gases.

habitat place where particular living things normally live

hybrid car powered by a combination of an electric motor and a small internal combustion engine

hydrocarbon chemical compound containing only carbon and hydrogen

incandescent light bulb bulb with a brightly glowing filament. It was the main kind of bulb used in homes for over 100 years, but it is now being replaced by low-energy bulbs.

internal combustion (IC) engine engine in which combustion (burning) is produced by causing an explosion of a mixture of fuel and air inside a small chamber called a cylinder

kinetic energy movement energy

oxide chemical compound produced when oxygen reacts with an element or other chemical

pesticide chemical sprayed on farm crops to kill insects or other pests that eat the crop

renewable can be replaced. Wood is a renewable fuel because new trees can be grown to replace those used as fuel.

slaughterhouse place where animals are killed for eating

smog choking mix of smoke and fog only usually found in cities

starch type of carbohydrate used by most plants as a food store

sustainable does not use up too many natural resources or pollute the environment

turbojet jet engine in which the jet gases also operate a turbine-driven compressor

FIND OUT MORE

Books

Bowden, Rob. *Transportation* (21st Century Debates). Chicago: Raintree, 2004.

Green, Jen. *Sustaining Our Natural Resources* (The Environment Challenge). Chicago: Raintree, 2011.

Laidlaw, Jill. *Cities* (Sustaining Our Environment). Mankato, Minn.: Amicus, 2011.

Senker, Cath. *Sustainable Transportation* (How Can We Save Our World?). Mankato, Minn.: Arcturus, 2010.

Solway, Andrew. *Designing Greener Vehicles and Buildings* (Why Science Matters). Chicago: Heinemann Library, 2009.

Web sites

Earth Day: The History of a Movement: **www.earthday.org/earth-day-history-movement**
Find information on the history of Earth Day and a video of the first Earth Day event.

EPA Green Vehicle Guide: **www.epa.gov/greenvehicles/Index.do**
This is a guide to fuel-efficient modern cars.

Shell Eco-Marathon: **www.shell.com/home/content/ecomarathon**
Learn more about events held around the world each year to find the most fuel-efficient vehicle in the world.

The World's Worst Traffic Jams: **www.time.com/time/world/article/0,8599,1733872,00.html**
This article in *Time* magazine is about traffic congestion around the world.

Earth Summit 2012: **www.uncsd2012.org/rio20**
This web site has details about the latest meeting of the United Nations Conference on Sustainable Development.

World Solar Challenge: **www.worldsolarchallenge.org**
This is the web site of the annual solar-powered car race across Australia.

DVD

Earth Days (PBS, 2010). This documentary made by the Public Broadcasting Service is about the first Earth Day and the start of the environmental movement in the United States.

Organizations

Earth Day Network
1616 P Street NW
Suite 340
Washington, D.C. 20036
www.earthday.org
The Earth Day Network works with many partners to mobilize the environmental movement. More than 1 billion people now participate in Earth Day activities each year.

Friends of the Earth
1100 15th Street NW
Washington, D.C. 20005
www.foe.org
Friends of the Earth was one of the first environmental organizations to campaign for the reduction of carbon emissions and the prevention of climate change.

United Nations Environment Program
www.unep.org
This is the UN organization concerned with reducing carbon emissions and protecting the environment.

U.S. Environmental Protection Agency
1200 Pennsylvania Avenue, NW
Washington, D.C. 20460
www.epa.gov
The EPA is the department of the U.S. government in charge of issues affecting the environment. Explore its web site to learn about the current state of issues like air pollution, as well as information about programs and technologies that can help improve the situation.

Other topics to research

Look at the labels on the food in your house. How far has the food traveled? Research how you could reduce food miles. Are there local farmers' markets in your area? What foods are grown or made locally?

Write a transportation diary. How many trips do you make by car each week? Do some research to find out how much carbon your trips emit. Are there ways in which you could reduce these emissions?

INDEX

Fidel Castro *(right)* and Che Guevara *(left)* made an unbeatable rebel combination in the 1950s and succeeded —where others had failed—in destroying a strong, U.S.-supported regime.

1958 Castro's call for a general strike failed to bring the Cuban economy to a halt but helped convince the U.S. government that Batista's days were numbered. The United States canceled all permits held by private companies to ship arms to Batista. Stubborn in the face of this loss of support,

Batista proceeded with plans to hold elections in November.

Most Cubans boycotted the balloting, which Andrés Agüero Rivero—Batista's hand-picked candidate—won. Batista then ordered his army to launch an overwhelming offensive to destroy the rebels. But his

Photo by Alfred Padula

Cuba's telephone authority is located in this building, which was formerly owned by the U.S. International Telephone and Telegraph Company (ITT). The Castro government took possession of the building after the 1959 revolution.

The Cuban Revolution

Castro was acclaimed with as much enthusiasm by the international community as he was by his own people. Against incredible odds, the guerrilla leader had succeeded in overthrowing a corrupt and well-armed government. A few people reserved their applause until Castro outlined his plans for the future. Castro was determined to make Cuba into a socialist nation. As a result, some of those who had fought shoulder to shoulder alongside Castro during the rebellion left the country in protest.

By the end of 1960, as the Castro government moved toward a state-controlled system, most foreign-owned and much Cuban-owned property was nationalized. Citizens of the United States were major losers in this transition to socialism. Their losses in sugar mills, banks, hotels, utility companies, mines, and farms were calculated to be about $2 billion.

To retaliate for these setbacks, the U.S. government stopped buying Cuban sugar—the mainstay of the island's economy. This decision was a devastating blow to Cuba, because sugar sales to the United States had been worth more than $500 million annually. Opposition to Castro developed when it became increasingly clear that he was determined to model his system of government after that of the Soviet Union and not of the West.

Under the new regime, the rights and interests of individual Cubans were less important than economic growth and social equality. Another goal, Castro declared, was to make Cuba a leader and supporter of wars of liberation elsewhere in Latin America and in other Third World nations.

The United States formally broke off all diplomatic relations with Cuba in January 1961, just two years after Castro had taken power. By then trade and commerce between the two countries had almost come to a complete halt.

forces, though well equipped and trained, refused to fight when confronted by an enemy with whom most of the troops sympathized. Batista's army defected.

After a sober stocktaking on New Year's Eve, Batista fled the country. In the early hours of January 1, 1959, he went first to the Dominican Republic and later to Portugal. Thousands of his supporters also left the country.

Courtesy of Tom Trow

A poster produced in Cuba emphasizes the Castro-regime view that the struggle of the Farabundo Martí National Liberation Front (FMLN) in El Salvador is another Third World fight for freedom.

The issue of African apartheid—racial separation—is addressed in this Cuban poster. It also can be viewed as part of Castro's bid to be a major leader of worldwide wars of liberation and anticolonialism.

Courtesy of Tom Trow

Photo by Alfred Padula

A captured plane from the Bay of Pigs invasion is on display at the Girón Museum in Playa Girón—the beachhead where the unsuccessful landing took place.

Cuba and the Cold War

As the number of Cuban defectors grew, the United States secretly trained and armed Cuban exiles for an invasion of their homeland. At the time of the training, the U.S. government was convinced that, once the rebels landed on Cuban shores, the Cuban people would join them and that Castro's army, like Batista's before him, would disband.

But this did not happen. On April 17, 1961, the invaders were quickly and easily defeated where they landed at the Bay of Pigs. Those who were not killed were taken to Cuban prisons, where some of them were to remain for more than 25 years. The anniversary of the victory is commemorated annually as the first major defeat of U.S. forces in the Western Hemisphere.

By the early 1960s, Cuba had formed a close alliance with the Soviet Union, a huge Communist state. Soviet leaders, who sought a strategic ally in the Western Hemisphere, supplied Cuba with financial aid, consumer goods, and energy supplies. By trading its valuable oil for Cuban sugar, the Soviet Union supported the Cuban economy, allowing Castro's regime to build new industries in the cities and to develop the island's agriculture.

Eight months after the Bay of Pigs, Castro declared, "I am a Marxist-Leninist and will be a Marxist-Leninist until the day I die." (A Marxist-Leninist follows the Communist doctrine developed by Karl Marx and V. I. Lenin.) A month later, the Organization of American States (OAS), an association of hemispheric nations, excluded Cuba from active membership.

The tension between the United States and Cuba dramatically worsened in the summer of 1962. Photographs taken by U.S. planes revealed that Cuba was receiving military equipment from the Soviet Union and that many Soviet technicians were arriving in Cuba. In October President Kennedy told the U.S. public that the Soviets were installing missile bases in Cuba capable of launching nuclear attacks against the United States, Central America, and parts of Mexico.

Kennedy demanded that the missiles be removed immediately and imposed a naval blockade of Cuba to enforce his demand. Tensions rose until the Soviets finally decided to remove their missiles.

In accepting the Soviet decision to dismantle missile bases, Castro suffered a loss of prestige. It became clear that Castro could be pressured by the Soviet Union on matters affecting East-West relations. Eventually the new dependency relationship also extended to the Cuban economy, whose survival—since the U.S. embargo on trade with Cuba—had been made possible only by large amounts of Soviet foreign aid.

Recent U.S.-Cuban Relations

The record of U.S.-Cuban relations over the past quarter century has been marked by mutual distrust and hostility. In the 1970s renewed signs of a possible thaw occurred. Working through Czechoslovakian and Swiss diplomatic intermediaries, the two countries worked out an agreement in

Aerial photography taken by U.S. planes in October of 1962 revealed the partial installation of missile sites at San Cristóbal in western Cuba.

1973 whereby Cuba punished hijackers of U.S. commercial aircraft. Previously hijackers had commanded pilots to fly to the safe sanctuary of Cuba. In 1975 the United States joined other hemispheric nations in voting to lift economic sanctions imposed against Cuba 21 years earlier by the Organization of American States.

In 1980 Castro temporarily allowed emigration. Discontent with Castro's policies motivated Cubans to assemble a flotilla of private vessels. The boats ferried some 125,000 Cubans from Mariel in Pinar del Río province to ports in Florida.

In 1987 the United States and Cuba agreed on the details for returning some of the refugees to Cuba. Despite the easing of restrictions on emigration, the Castro government still bans political meetings, prohibits opposition parties, and uses a large network of police spies.

In the fall of 1991, the breakup of the Soviet Union and the fall of the Soviet government led to a suspension of aid. No longer supported by trade with the Soviet Union and eastern Europe, the Cuban economy began to collapse. With no currency to buy imports, Cuba could not afford imported consumer goods, spare parts, gasoline, and food, all of which became scarce and expensive.

Faced with worsening social unrest, the government passed economic reforms in the mid-1990s. Certain workers could be self-employed, and farmers were free to sell crops on the open market. The government permitted foreign investment in some industries. Despite the opening of the economy, Cuba's government remains closed to opposition parties. Castro seems determined to preserve the strictly Communist regime that he founded in the late 1950s.

U.S. Coast Guard Photo

In the 1980s boats carrying large numbers of Cuban emigrants began arriving in southern Florida from Mariel, Cuba. Many of the newcomers remained in and around Miami, which is now the U.S. city with the largest Cuban population.

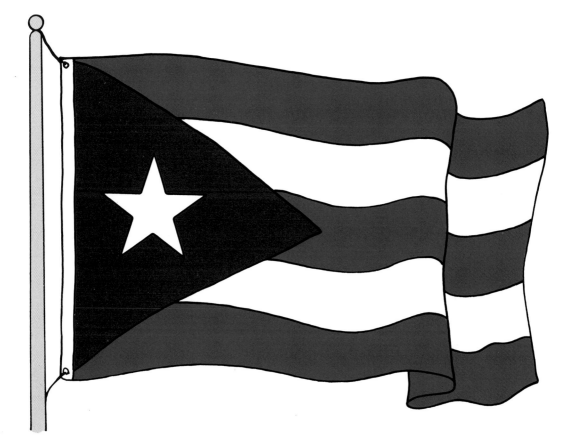

The Cuban flag was officially adopted in 1902, but it was designed earlier at the request of Narciso López, who had organized three unsuccessful attempts to secure Cuban independence.

Government

Under the 1976 constitution, the Republic of Cuba consists of 14 provinces and 169 municipalities. The Communist party of Cuba is the only legal political party. A central committee and a politburo of 24 members supervises party affairs.

Fidel Castro, as the president of the Council of State, is the head of the Cuban government. The president directs the councils of state and of ministers and also serves as the commander of the armed forces. Castro shares power only with his brother, Raul, and with a few associates.

The Cuban legislature is a unicameral (one-house) body called the National Assembly of People's Power. The Assembly appoints the members of the two governing councils. Assembly members—all of whom belong to the Communist party—are elected by a direct popular vote to five-year terms. Cuba also has municipal, regional, and provincial assemblies.

The People's Supreme Court is the highest judicial body, and its four separate chambers hear cases dealing with offenses against criminal, civil, military, and state security laws.

Picking fruit in teams of two is part of the combined work-study curriculum of many Cuban schools.

Photo by Lois M. Smith

3)   The People

Cuba's population of 11 million makes it the most populous island in the Caribbean. The nation's growth rate of 0.7 percent—relatively low for Caribbean nations—will double the number of inhabitants in 102 years. Large numbers of Cubans have emigrated in recent years, as residents seek economic opportunities in other nations, particularly the United States.

Ethnic Groups

Official figures classify the Cuban population as 66 percent white, 12 percent black, and 22 percent of mixed ancestry. But all such estimates of ethnic composition in Cuba are subject to substantial margins of error. Various races have intermarried on the Caribbean island, making it impossible to classify the resulting population mixture with total accuracy. It can be said, however, that there are no full-blooded Indians on the island.

Since the conquest of Cuba by Spain, the number of Spanish-descended people has been periodically increased through immigration. Historically Cuba has provided asylum to refugees from Hispanic lands, and this trend continues to the present day. Large numbers of Spaniards settled on the island during the 1936–1939 Spanish civil war. In recent years Cuba has opened its doors to political refugees from many Latin American nations.

As elsewhere in the Caribbean, communities of Chinese, Lebanese, and East Indian settlers have arrived in Cuba. Spanish-descended Cubans continue to hold most of the important posts in government and commerce, while blacks have remained at the bottom of economic, social, and cultural ladders, despite the Castro regime's claim of having achieved full equality.

Religion

Like other Marxist governments, the Castro regime seeks to de-emphasize the role of religion in everyday life and—even though it maintains diplomatic relations with the Vatican—has officially classified the country as atheistic. Nonetheless, many Cubans today remain faithful Roman Catholics. They are baptized, married, and buried with the Church's guidance. Protestant faiths have attracted only about 3 or 4 percent of the Cuban population.

The Castro regime has consistently downgraded the Christian tradition—expelling bishops, taking over church-run schools, and barring Christians from government and university jobs. The Castro government has even discouraged the observance of Christmas because this holiday occurs during the all-important sugarcane harvest. Moreover, their Christian faith disqualifies many Cubans from Communist

Photo by Marty Nordstrom

Despite the Castro regime's attempt to de-emphasize the role of the Roman Catholic Church, many Cubans—mostly of the older generation—are still devoted believers.

A Havana church undergoes renovation, which suggests that the Castro government has relaxed its anti-Church policies to some degree.

Day-care centers, like Grandes Alamedas in Havana, provide food, clothing, and medical attention to children aged 45 days to 5 years.

party membership. Yet the new liberation theology seems to attract Castro, who was reared in a Catholic home. (Liberation theology refers to a contemporary movement that attempts to improve social and political conditions in developing countries, often within a religious framework.) The Cuban leader opposed the Church initially because it harbored counterrevolutionries. But Castro regards liberation theology as an ally in his efforts to gain allies in Latin America and in building a Communist society in Cuba.

Population

Despite government efforts to encourage farmers to stay on the land, 74 percent of Cuba's people live in urban areas. Unlike most other Latin American nations, however, Cuba's population is nearly stable. Cuba owes this stability to the emigration —mainly to the United States—of more than a million dissatisfied Cubans.

With improvements in health care, Cuba's population is heavily weighted at the age extremes—those either too young or too old to work. Presently 22 percent of the population is under age 15 while 9 percent is over age 65. Roughly one-fourth of the population makes up the work force, whereas 40 percent does so in the United States. However, compared to other nations in Latin America, Cuba's percentage (44) of economically active citizens is high. Costa Rica, with whom Cuba is sometimes statistically compared, has a figure of 20.7 percent, while industrialized Brazil's figure is 26.6 percent.

The Arts

Cuban culture, which once was criticized by some Cubans for adopting forms and ideas from other parts of the world—most notably from Europe—is now directed toward themes concerning the former European colonies. To some extent this trend draws on historical Cuban realities.

In a novel called *Cecilia Valdés o la loma del angel* (Cecilia Valdés or the angel's hillock) published in 1882, Cirilo Villaverde wrote of a tragic love affair between a mulatto woman and a Spanish-Cuban aristocrat. The novel, which exposed social inequality and the harsh life of Cubans under Spanish rule, is widely read in Cuban schools.

AFRO-CUBANISM

The twentieth century ushered in strong and original literary ideas in Cuba. Over a period of 50 years, Fernando Ortiz, founder of the Society of Afro-Cuban Studies in 1926, developed Cuban pride and understanding of black contributions to the island's culture.

By the 1920s many other leading literary figures had taken up the Afro-Cuban cause as a means of developing an authentic Cuban national identity. In his first novel, *¡Ecué-Yamba-O!,* Alejo Carpentier highlighted scenes in the lives of Afro-Cubans.

African elements dominated the new music from Cuba—even the new rhythms that developed along classical lines. In 1932 Gonzalo Roig, founder of Havana's symphony orchestra, adapted Villaverde's novel *Cecilia Valdés* as an operetta. He used dances such as the rumba, *guaracha,* tango, conga, *contradanza,* and *habanera* to present the lively and sensual style of Spanish-Cuban music. Some of the words of the operetta were sung in Afro-Cuban idioms whose meaning was impossible to translate exactly. The success of the work at concert halls in several countries brought further recognition to the Afro-Cubanist movement, which enjoyed a widespread popularity from about 1926 to 1940 and which still has admirers today.

The 1930s through 1950s also witnessed the emergence of Marxist themes in Cuban literature and art. The Marxist influence was foreseen in the poem *"La zafra"* (The sugarcane harvest), published by Agustín Acosta in 1926. The poem depicts the life

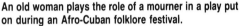
Independent Picture Service

An old woman plays the role of a mourner in a play put on during an Afro-Cuban folklore festival.

Independent Picture Service

A Cuban drummer beats a rhythm brought to the island by African slaves.

Independent Picture Service

Professional Cuban dancers perform a work taken from a traditional dance of the Yoruba tribe of West Africa.

49

of sugar workers under capitalism. Other leading literary figures—such as the poet Nicolás Guillén, who won the Lenin Prize in 1956—seek to channel the exploration of African roots into Marxist paths. In his poetry, Guillén expresses the hopes and frustrations of the exploited classes. Guillén lived to be honored by his country and to become the first president of the Union of Writers and Artists after it was founded in 1961.

AFTER THE CASTRO REVOLUTION

Since 1959 the Castro government has sought to make culture serve the state. Artists from all fields are encouraged to justify their work in terms of the goals of the revolution, the needs of the people, and the national interest.

All controlled Cuban media—the press, radio, and television—likewise emphasize the accomplishment of revolutionary goals. Under the Castro regime, no criticism of the government is permitted, except for occasional and extremely forthright comments uttered by Castro himself and, to some limited extent, by lesser officials. All information is filled with propaganda and promotes Marxist ideology.

Despite rigid control of all media, some Cuban artistic forms have found an admiring audience at home and abroad. One of these forms is poster art. Under Castro, posters have become a prime vehicle for communicating with the masses, and artists of considerable talent have been attracted to poster production.

Another area of achievement is Cuban cinema. On modest budgets, Cuban filmmakers have produced excellent short films; many of them are remarkably candid and moving documentaries on social and political themes. The films have competed successfully at festivals throughout the world, such as in Moscow, Leipzig, and London.

Cuban architects, too, have become innovators in designing low-cost, prefabricated villages as a contribution toward solving the nation's housing shortage. And Cuban builders have become remarkably skilled in the use of these standardized housing components. Furthermore, they have pioneered in the construction of educational complexes to accommodate

ICAIC poster Courtesy of Tom Trow

A poster produced by the Instituto Cubano del Arte y Industria Cinematográficos (ICAIC) advertises the film *Que Levante La Mano La Guitarra* (The guitar raises its hand), about music as a means of political and social expression.

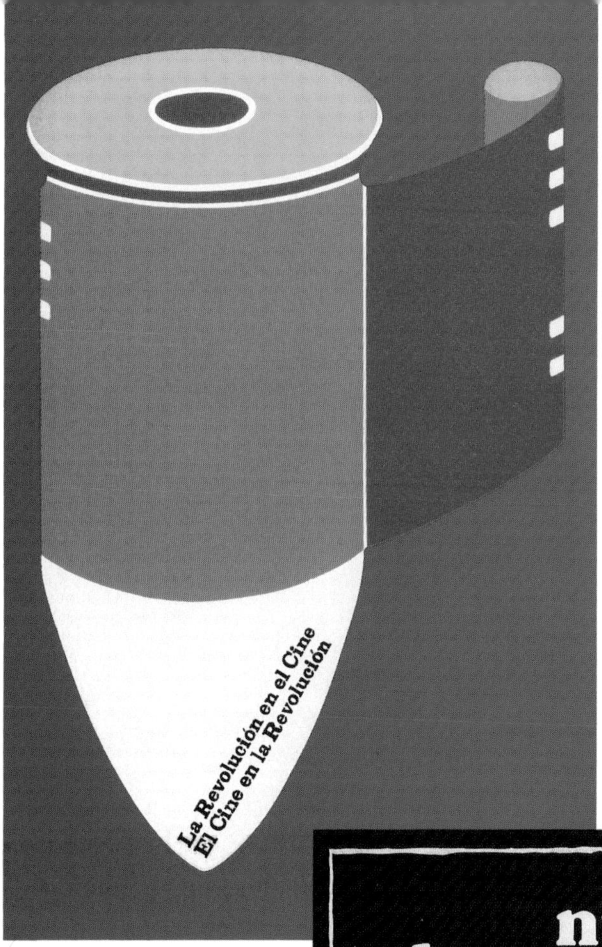

A roll of film becomes a powerful bullet and visually expresses the theme of a recent Cuban cinema series: The revolution on film, and film in the revolution.

La Revolución en el Cine
El Cine en la Revolución

ICAIC poster Courtesy of Tom Trow

niños desaparecidos
missing children
UN DOCUMENTAL DE ESTELA BRAVO

ICAIC poster Courtesy of Tom Trow

The Cuban film *niños desaparecidos* (missing children) won a recent international documentary award for its treatment of the problem of missing Argentinian children, whose parents have been jailed for disagreeing with the government.

large numbers of students at schools and universities.

Sports

Cubans, including Castro, are very interested in athletics. Castro's government has promoted sports and fitness as a matter of national policy. Cuban athletes play most games familiar to people in other countries—soccer and tennis, for example—and are keen competitors. Sports that have their origins in the United States are very popular—especially baseball, softball, and basketball. During the baseball season, most open spaces have games in progress. Baseball players of Cuban origin have played on major league teams in the United States. In addition, Cubans have achieved international distinction in boxing, rowing, sailing, and swimming.

Health

Even before the Castro revolution, Cuba's death rate and infant mortality rate were

Photo by Lois M. Smith

Workers at this plant in Havana province produce the prefabricated housing units used throughout Cuba. The Cuban government seeks to solve a housing shortage by mass-producing homes.

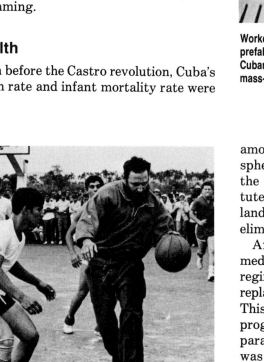
Independent Picture Service

Occasionally, Castro has time to indulge in a favorite sport—basketball.

among the lowest in the Western Hemisphere. With U.S. assistance, Cuba was the first Latin American nation to institute a public health department. The island also was one of the first countries to eliminate malaria.

After 1959, however, many qualified medical personnel left Cuba, and the new regime was faced with the problem of replacing them with trained professionals. This feat was accomplished through faster programs in all medical fields, including paramedical practices. In 1993 the ratio was 215 patients for every physician.

These improvements gave Cuba one of the best health records in the Caribbean region. Infant mortality—the number of babies who die within a year of birth—is 9.4 per 1,000. Life expectancy is 75 years.

All medical services are free in Cuba; private practice was abolished by the Castro government. Health-care personnel are distributed fairly evenly throughout the country, due in part to requirements that medical practitioners devote part of their time to work in rural regions. Shortages of medicines and basic supplies, however, still affect the health system. In addition, malnutrition threatens areas where the government has imposed food rationing.

Families, Women, and Children

Cuban family relationships are strong and warm, especially between the young and old. Families are closely knit, with meaningful relationships extending even to distant cousins. Included in the extended family are business associates and carefully selected godparents, both of whom provide wise counsel and support in the rearing and education of children.

Traditionally Cuban women were sheltered in a male-centered social order, but they are replacing men in factories and in government positions. By law, Cuba's system of day nurseries offers care to all children 45 days or older.

Teenage pregnancies constituted the majority of births in seven provinces according to a recent government survey. As a result, the Castro government energetically promotes birth control methods. By 1996, nearly 90 percent of married women were using some form of birth control—one of the highest figures in the world.

Education

The literacy rate in Cuba has often been higher than the rates of many other Third World countries. In 1953, for example, only 10 percent of Haiti's population could read and write, while in the same period, the figure was about 80 percent in Cuba.

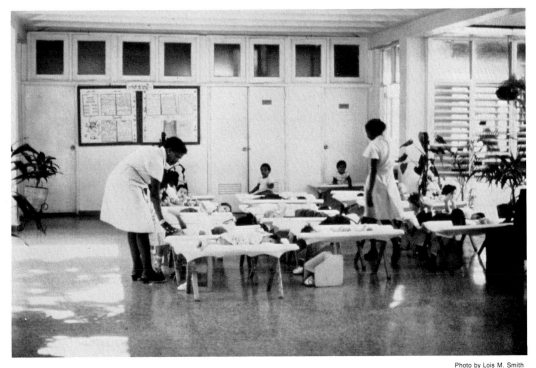

Photo by Lois M. Smith

Between the hours of 7:00 A.M. and 7:00 P.M., children of working mothers receive excellent attention at day-care centers.

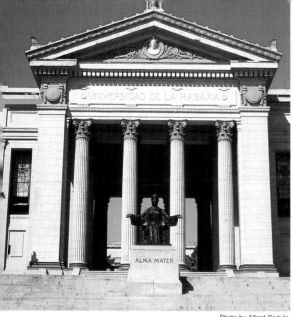

Many students of the University of Havana—including Fidel Castro, who earned his law degree there in 1950—have used its steps as a speaker's platform.

Education is free and compulsory between the ages of 6 and 12. After the age of 12, school attendance is optional. Most curricula include work and study—a combination of practical labor and classroom instruction. Spanish is the language of instruction, but students are also taught Russian and English.

At all levels of education, Marxist-Leninist dogma is emphasized. The Cuban government requires teachers to attend classes on Communist theory at national training centers; even medical school students are required to take courses in Communist doctrine before being allowed to practice medicine.

Four universities exist in Cuba, the largest of which is the University of Havana. Courses emphasize technology, agriculture, vocational training, and teacher training. According to recent figures, Cuba ranks among the highest worldwide in the amount (10 percent) of its gross national product used for education.

Since the inauguration of a literacy campaign in 1961, the national literacy rate in Cuba has risen to 94 percent.

Students at Cuban secondary schools are taught a wide variety of courses—including English and Marxism.

A view of the harbor of Santiago de Cuba during the 1980s shows ships from the Soviet Union in port. Since the Soviet Union dissolved and ended its aid, Cuba has lacked many vital supplies.

4)   The Economy

In the years following Castro's revolution, the Cuban economy became closely tied to the Soviet Union and to the Communist nations of eastern Europe. In a system of barter (trade without money), the Soviet government shipped oil, grain, and raw materials to Cuba in exchange for sugar. Because world market prices for sugar were falling, and prices for oil rose, this trade in effect supported Cuba's economy with a generous subsidy.

With the collapse of the Soviet Union in 1991, however, the barter of vital commodities for sugar ended. Cuba's trade with Russia and other former members of the Soviet bloc was put on a cash basis, at market prices. This action devastated the Cuban economy. Supplies of energy, consumer goods, and food sharply declined, and prices steadily rose. In addition, the continuing United States embargo against trade with Cuba hurt the island's economy.

The Cuban economy recovered somewhat in the mid-1990s. The gross domestic product (GDP)—the amount of goods and services produced in a year—increased by small amounts in 1994 and 1995, after falling sharply for several years. To bring its budget deficit under control, the government raised taxes as well as prices on goods. Many factories reopened under foreign ownership, and the tourism sector prospered, letting many Cubans find steady employment. In addition, Cuba prepared to open some free-trade zones, which will permit companies to manufacture and export their goods free of export taxes.

Sugarcane Harvest

The sugarcane harvest is the most crucial annual event in the Cuban economy. The Castro government takes pride in its success in mechanizing much of the sugarcane harvest. Mechanical harvesters, which look like huge beetles, cut the cane on level land. When there are irregularities in the landscape, however, the stalks must still be cut by hand—a task that, pre- or post-revolution, is backbreaking work.

Ninety percent of the production at most mills is sugar; the balance comprises molasses and bagasse (the residue left after sugarcane is ground). Bagasse, be-

sides its usefulness as a source of energy, also figures in the production of paper, wallboard, and other products. Mill managers receive salaries equivalent to $500 a month. The average mill or field worker receives $200 a month. The salaries are low, but workers in Cuba's Marxist society also receive bonuses such as free housing and appliances.

One-Crop Economy

The sugar crop has been the single most important component of Cuba's economy throughout much of its history. During centuries of Spanish rule, sugar remained the island's leading export, and sugar production was built into the very fabric of Cuban life. Large numbers of unskilled workers and large tracts of land were required for the operation of a profitable sugarcane estate. Thus, like other areas of the world where the economy depended on large-acreage crops, Cuban society was divided at an early date into plantation owners and plantation workers.

Photo by Robert M. Levine

Overseers of early twentieth-century sugarcane plantations directed the work of unskilled laborers and reported to the estate owners.

In 1857 black slaves were still at work in sugar mills. Slavery was not completely abolished in Cuba until 1886.

Spanish overlords enjoyed luxurious homes, vacations abroad, and a fine education for their children. The blacks, who were brought in bondage to cut the cane, led a hard life in miserable working and living conditions on the owner's estate.

The operation of this arrangement was interrupted only once before the 1959 revolution, when U.S. military authorities, who ruled the island between 1898 and 1902 after the Spanish-American War, abolished the plantation system. The way was cleared for increased ownership of the sugarcane-producing lands and sugar mills by local Cuban interests. During this transitional period, thousands of independent tenant farmers became owners of small plots of land.

The old economic system was revived, however, when large, U.S.-owned corporations moved into the vacuum created by the departure of the Spanish plantation owners. Tenant farmers were bought out by large sugarcane mills, which, along with

Good schools, plenty of food, and fine clothing awaited the children of the sugar barons.

the largest tracts of land, were owned by corporations. The prosperity of Cuba's sugar industry remained dependent on the prices paid for sugar in world commerce. For Cuba this reliance on world sugar prices, over which Cuba has had little or no control, has meant periods of "boom or bust" as the prices have risen sharply or dropped suddenly.

Since the revolution, the Castro government has assumed complete control over sugar production. The government sought to ease the manual labor required to produce sugar. As in the past, however, many Cubans feel that the earnings from sugar do not adequately compensate them for their labor in raising the crop. With the end of Soviet support of sugar exports, fuel and machinery have become increasingly scarce. Many sugar plantations have reverted to manual cutting. In addition, mills have closed and many farmers now must transport their crop by animal-driven carts.

Castro's revolution also brought about the nationalization of agriculture. After taking control of 70 percent of Cuba's farmland, the Cuban regime set up an extensive system of state farms. In 1993, many state farms became private cooperatives. Most crops must be sold to the state at fixed prices, but the government allows small, open markets for surpluses. In addition, workers themselves are now allowed to manage their farms.

Cuba's soil and climate support a wide variety of food crops, including bananas, citrus foods, tomatoes, coffee, and sweet potatoes. Staple crops include potatoes and rice. Most tobacco plantations operate in the western province of Pinar del Rio. The government supports extensive cattle-herding. Farmers also raise pigs, sheep, goats, horses, and poultry.

Manufacturing

Like other Communist states, the Castro government nationalized industry by seiz-

Courtesy of Norman Sherman

As a means of viewing the cane harvest as a national priority, a colorful poster in Havana depicts Che Guevara as a hardworking cutter.

ing property and placing production under the control of large state bureaucracies. With help from the Soviet bloc, Cuba was able to produce cement, steel, fertilizer, tires, baseballs, textiles, and a wide variety of consumer goods.

The Soviet government shipped many of the raw materials which Cuban factories processed into finished goods. For example, a large refrigerator plant on the outskirts of Santa Clara used Soviet plastic and steel to make its products. When raw

58

materials did not arrive in time, production at the plant ceased—although workers still received 70 percent of their salaries. Workers also benefited from an elaborate system of incentives, with bonuses such as extra pay, cars, and travel provided for those who exceeded production quotas.

The breakup of the Soviet Union in 1991 put an end to Soviet supplies and financial support. The other former Communist nations of eastern Europe are providing neither raw materials nor a dependable market for finished goods. The Cuban government has been forced to close factories and lay off thousands of workers, many of whom now work at manual labor in the countryside.

To revive manufacturing in Cuba, Castro is seeking joint business ventures with companies in western Europe and Latin America. Cuba's low wage rates

Women are increasingly working shoulder to shoulder with men in Cuban factories. Here, a young woman learns to handle a lathe.

Baseballs are fairly recent items on Cuba's list of manufactured goods. This industry developed quickly because of the popularity of the sport on the island.

make the island an attractive place for foreign companies to establish manufacturing facilities. To encourage such investment, in 1995 Cuba legalized foreign plant ownership.

Trade

During the 1980s, Cuba imported 90 percent of its energy, as well as essential transportation goods such as buses, trucks, and spare parts. Basic foods—including rice, wheat, vegetable oils, and beans—also had to be imported. Most of the country's foreign trade was with the Soviet Union and with the Soviet-bloc countries.

Cuban trade suffered a heavy blow with the ending of this Soviet-bloc support. The country could not pay for imports and could offer only a few manufactured goods, sugar, and minerals as exports. As a result, the trade deficit worsened throughout the early and mid-1990s.

Despite the loss of Soviet support, the United States government continues to impose a strict embargo on trade with Cuba. This means that Cuba has no access to a huge market that lies just 90 miles from the island's northern ports. To compensate, the Castro government is seeking to expand its trade with other Latin American countries. The regime may also be able to attract hard currency by developing Cuba's tourism industry, which grew rapidly in the mid-1990s.

The future of Cuban exports depends on joint ventures to develop the island's natural resources, which include nickel, cobalt, iron ore, managanese, timber, and agricultural products—seafood, coffee, citrus fruits, tobacco, and rum. Cuba also continues to manufacture Havana cigars, which many consider the finest in the world. Cuban cigars, which are rolled by hand in small factories by skilled workers, have long been an important source of foreign revenue.

Photo by Alfred Padula

A cowboy in eastern Cuba rounds up his herd. Cattle now number more than 5.9 million head, due largely to a new breeding program instituted by the Castro government.

By greatly expanding its fleet, Cuba's nationalized fishing industry has finally begun to take advantage of the island's geographic location in the middle of major migrations of sea life. Cuban fishing cooperatives net tuna, shellfish, and bonito, a fish common in tropical waters.

The Future

Fidel Castro traded on Cuba's strategic location in the Caribbean to gain the alliance of powerful Communist states in Europe. The Cuban government was successful in improving education and health conditions for many Cuban citizens. As economic conditions worsened in the

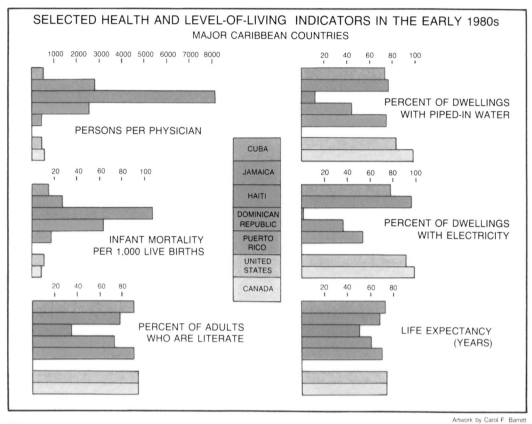

SELECTED HEALTH AND LEVEL-OF-LIVING INDICATORS IN THE EARLY 1980s
MAJOR CARIBBEAN COUNTRIES

PERSONS PER PHYSICIAN

PERCENT OF DWELLINGS WITH PIPED-IN WATER

CUBA
JAMAICA
HAITI
DOMINICAN REPUBLIC
PUERTO RICO
UNITED STATES
CANADA

INFANT MORTALITY PER 1,000 LIVE BIRTHS

PERCENT OF DWELLINGS WITH ELECTRICITY

PERCENT OF ADULTS WHO ARE LITERATE

LIFE EXPECTANCY (YEARS)

Artwork by Carol F. Barrett

This graph shows how greatly each of six factors, which are suggestive of the quality of life, varies among the five major Caribbean countries. The United States and Canada are included for comparison. Data from *UN Statistical Yearbook 1982, 1984 UN Demographic Yearbook, 1986 Britannica Book of the Year*, and "1986 World Population Data Sheet."

Bohíos, or straw-thatched huts, are among the most common dwellings of people in the Cuban countryside.

1980s, however, Castro often criticized and punished his aides for poor management and corruption. The president dismissed three once-trusted supporters from high posts in the government, and in 1989 executed several military leaders for their open criticism of the regime.

Yet the sharp decline of living standards and the collapse of Cuba's economy has placed more focus on the quality of Castro's own leadership. Although many Cubans still strongly support Cuba's socialist system, opposition to Castro, especially in the cities, is increasing. The powerful Cuban army remains loyal to the regime, however, and stands ready to crush any open revolt.

Seeking solutions to the country's problems, the Cuban government is trying to

Grafitti is uncommon in Cuba, but a small, hidden corner was found to express the belief that the national debt is unpayable.

develop new aspects of the economy. Hotels have been built to accommodate a growing number of tourists, and Cuba's leaders have succeeded in persuading foreign companies to make large investments in Cuba.

Despite the fall of many Communist regimes in Europe, Castro holds strongly to his vision of a Communist Cuba. Although Cuba's first parliamentary elections took place in February 1993, all candidates belonged to the Communist party, which remain's Cuba's only legal political organization.

Cuba's economic future, however, remains uncertain. Despite the continuing U.S. embargo, the government's new policies have ended the steep economic decline. Opening up the country to foreign investment may end some of Cuba's isolation. Even so, poverty continues to be widespread. An improving economy may allow the Cuban Communist party to maintain its hold on power into the twenty-first century.

The Havana-registered *Presidente Allende,* named after the socialist president of Chile who was killed in a 1973 coup, steams into Havana Harbor.

Index